My Sweet Guillotine

SHAKESPEARE AND COMPANY
KILOMETER ZERO PARIS

My
Sweet
Guillotine

Jayne
Tuttle

Hardie Grant

BOOKS

Published in 2022 by Hardie Grant Books, an imprint of Hardie Grant Publishing

Hardie Grant Books (Melbourne)
Wurundjeri Country
Building 1, 658 Church Street
Richmond, Victoria 3121

Hardie Grant Books (London)
5th & 6th Floors
52–54 Southwark Street
London SE1 1UN

hardiegrantbooks.com

 A catalogue record for this
book is available from the
NATIONAL
LIBRARY National Library of Australia
OF AUSTRALIA

My Sweet Guillotine
ISBN 978 1 74379 785 3

10 9 8 7 6 5 4 3 2 1

Cover design by Jo Thomson
Cover image: Igor Ustynskyy/Women via Getty Images; Kisialiou Yury/Shutterstock.com
Typeset in 11/15pt Minion Pro by Cannon Typesetting
Printed in Australia by Griffin Press, an Accredited ISO AS/NZS 14001
Environmental Management System printer.

 The paper this book is printed on is certified against the Forest Stewardship
Council® Standards. Griffin Press holds FSC® chain of custody certification
SGSHK-COC-005088. FSC® promotes environmentally responsible, socially
beneficial and economically viable management of the world's forests.

Hardie Grant acknowledges the Traditional Owners of the country on which we work,
the Wurundjeri people of the Kulin nation and the Gadigal people of the Eora nation,
and recognises their continuing connection to the land, waters and culture. We pay our
respects to their Elders past and present.

For Matt and Frankie

La brume
laisse à l'imagination
le soin de terminer
l'image

Fog
leaves the imagination
to complete
the image

—Jacques Lecoq

Vertigo

There's a time of day in the rue du Château-d'Eau when the low sun hits the narrow street so fiercely you're blinded and have to keep walking until the world returns to you. If you were to stop during the blind-out you'd remain in a state of sightlessness and be bumped by a pram, a dog, or an older gent coming from the other direction who, oblivious to your inability to see, will huff and curse *fait chier* beneath his breath. When I first walked down this street and the blinding happened, the incapacity to see stopped me in my tracks. But now, delirious from a 21-hour flight, I stride into the abyss, the rays reminding my jetlagged body it is day, the smell of smoke and piss and burnt corn telling me I'm back.

My heart races in the blindness. Not just for the thrill of the void but for fear of being bumped. The break has healed, the doctors say, but the terror put into me about the consequences of the slightest neck movement has stayed in my body. As my sight returns, the figures and buildings in front of me are cast in silhouette, then colour gradually seeps back, rendering the garbage trucks and cars and *motos* and people more crisp and bright than ever. My heartbeat slows. What is different? I am different. Nothing is different. I am not different. I turn onto the rue du Faubourg-Saint-Denis, the street I spent almost every day on for two years. The Napoléon is still there

1

with new shiny tables, the *tabac presse*, the Mouton Blanc, the Château d'Eau bar with the 'eau's still out so the sign reads CHAT. It's like I never left. Never finished theatre school, never moved to the 20ᵗʰ, never got near-beheaded, never spent four months in Australia being nursed by my dad. I am always on this street. Even in Australia for those months I was always here in Bosch's *Garden of Earthly Delights*, the mess of bodies in all their lives, busy, bored, mad, sad. When I closed my eyes I could see every shop front, every doorway. Because I walked it, perhaps. When you walk, you see.

I thought Nadine would suggest we meet elsewhere, somewhere not so familiar, so full of recent memories, but I didn't argue, there's always reason to Nadine's rhyme. It does make sense to re-enter Paris from this place, I suppose, where I was happy not so long ago, far from any memory of the 20ᵗʰ and what happened. Where every day I'd rush to school in my theatre blacks, where Nadine and I and Adrien and Kiki and Harry and our theatre school friends would eat and drink and loiter. The parties, the pigeons, the people, always people in your way. Myself right now in a street mirror, a being in shards. Someone else. So thin she looks almost Parisian, but for the pale, ex-hospital vibe. Face not on quite right. I step in closer – it's normal to do that here, check one's lipstick, one's hair; mirrors everywhere to remind us we exist. The chin scar is like a sucked noodle squashed into the bottom of my face – I have to bring my lower lip upwards to notice it properly, but it does look like I have a permanent small piece of food stuck to my chin. The part where my teeth came through the skin below my lip is still a jagged black line – for some reason it stayed black even after they removed the stitches. The *pièce de résistance*, the scar that lightning bolts from my ear down my cheekbone, is still very visible, though less so with my hair down like this. I pull my hair back and turn my head to one side. The sun catches the damaged cheekbone and the sides of the cuts, highlighting the crevices. Badass, I tell myself. You're a badass scar-faced bitch. Rock that scar you badass. I cover it back up with hair.

No students outside the theatre school smoking cigarettes, leaning on bikes. Classes must be finished for the day, or, being Friday, everyone is inside watching *autocours*, or perhaps rehearsals for a *soirée*, the students in blacks, the *profs* with their legs crossed. I walk up to the old blue door and touch the small gold plaque that reads ÉCOLE INTERNATIONALE DE THÉÂTRE JACQUES LECOQ, as though pressing it will make something happen: time turn back, a new world emerge. Nothing happens, it's just a plaque. I peer through a gap in the door; no movement in the walkway. I always thought I'd miss school intensely after I finished but I hadn't, not a bit. Nostalgia implies unfinished business, or something you can't have again that you want: I had left every living, breathing scrap of myself inside that *Grande Salle*, that *Salle Verte*, those sweaty, sticky halls, in front of those cutting, discerning teachers. There had been nothing to miss.

My hands tremble. Funk of plane food in my mouth, jetlag blinking me in and out of reality. Should have gone to sleep for a bit at Nadine's like she said, though Kiki insists it's always better on arrival day to try and see it through, at least until dark.

Nadine said to meet her at 6 as she hurried out the door after meeting me on the canal and taking me up the seven flights of stairs to her new flat – if you can call it that – a carpeted walkway with a shower, no kitchen and two tiny rooms with a roof so low you almost have to crawl. I said Belleville. She said Jeannette. She likes their chicken salad. I said who would eat at Jeannette with the kitchen so close to that rancid toilet, but she said it's good as she pulled on her shoes, and once Nadine gets an idea in her mind there's no budging it. She set her alarm loud for 5 pm and told me *sleep*, but I was afraid I would never wake up and miss these precious days of homecoming.

Five days in Paris. A month in Portugal on the play. Then a month's residency back here at the Récollets, my old home, thanks to the sponsorship Marie-France secured for the play from the Ville de Paris. Enough time to find a new flat before *la rentrée*, a little place of my own, even a *chambre de bonne*. I lay on Nadine's mattress and took her ibuprofen and took in her world. It felt good to be back, but not quite, yet. Things of mine were scattered through the place amongst hers: my blue vase, my green fern, my red chair – my throne. The thought of my things having a life in Paris without me was disconcerting. I tried not to be nostalgic about them.

Couldn't sleep. I got up, showered, put on clothes, took them off, pulled on a green dress of Nadine's from a pile at the end of the bed, and wound my thick brown winter scarf around my neck until it was comfortably tight. Then I walked carefully down her slippery stairs and out along the Quai de Jemmapes, over the Bridge of Atmosphère and up past the Récollets, thought of going in and saying hello to Chantal, decided not yet and cut down the alleys towards the boulevard, taking my time, looking up. I walked these streets for years and never looked up, you don't look *up*, you're in too much of a hurry, and also when you were here as an au pair at 22 you looked up so much you were seen as a tourist and men pinched your butt.

On the corner of Château d'Eau and Strasbourg I stopped at Kiki's tree, the artwork she pointed out once that I'd passed a thousand times without noticing. Kiki always looked up. She never graduated from tourist and was not about to let some butt-pinching dick ruin her moment. The painting is an exact replica of the tall plane tree planted into the concrete in front of it. Such a work, and so easy to miss on the crammed, polluted boulevard. As the plane tree changes through the seasons, the painted memory of itself at its leafiest endures behind it. Now summer-full, the tree and its image were in perfect symmetry. Kiki's the shadow, me the tree, I thought to myself, imagining Kiki's laughter if I said that out loud. Paris is still not the same without her. I stood too long and looked, I don't care, pinch my butt. I'm in less danger of having my butt pinched now I'm 31, *femme. Madame.* Also, the scars.

⁓

Chez Jeannette is the same but cleaner, and Jeannette is gone. That is, if the old woman who tended the bar ever was Jeannette – I just assumed she was. Perhaps Jeannette was her favourite movie star. Perhaps it was her mother. There's a young guy behind the bar now, wild dark curls, that easygoing look of a Parisian who's travelled a lot. He lights a cigarette and I think of lighting one too, but the doctor told me 100% not to and the image he painted of the smoke going straight to the break in my neck makes me queasy.

The toilet is the same. The place is full of Adriens. Old Adrien, book-reading Adrien, girl Adrien. There is no way he would be hanging around the 10th, so it's unlikely I'll actually see him. The thought of him makes my heart thump, not for lust but the knowledge that if I ever do see him again, I will kill him. Now I can smell him. *Habit Rouge*. Perhaps I'm imagining it. Perhaps it's the guy at the table next to me, reading Beckett's *Happy Days* in English. A Lecoq student, I bet. It's one of my favourite plays, Winnie stuck in her mound, day after day, the sun baking down, her little bag with its revolver reminding her and us she can always end it. Where is Nadine? Should have brought a book. Nadine always takes a book everywhere she goes. Why didn't I bring a book? A strong bout of surrealness. I focus on the *kir* in front of me, squeeze my eyes awake. The Lecoq guy shifts in his loose black clothes, sending a waft of Adrien my way. I try to ignore the confusion it's creating in me, anger, nostalgia, sex. Unusual for an Englishman to wear *Habit Rouge*. Perhaps he's French reading Beckett in English. Doubtful.

'That guy smells like Adrien,' I say to Nadine as she sits down, not apologising for being late. She's not, I suppose, by Paris standards. A glass of *chablis* appears in front of her with a glass of nuts. The Beckett guy buries deeper into his book. Forgot he was English and can understand me perfectly. Nadine looks at him and I regret having said anything, as she leans towards me and sniffs deep, looking around like a detective. She can't smell anything, she says, but urine cakes and beer. Also, nice dress. She sends her wine back. The fresh glass is better. The new guy, named Grég, doesn't mind at all. Nadine smiles. She has had her blonde hair cut boy-short à la Jean Seberg, which suits her petite pixie face. She is less polished than before, more natural, though her teeth are still a brilliant white. She has lost skin. If I put on weight, Adrien would say that I had taken skin – *tu as pris de la peau*. I wouldn't say either to Nadine. Her skin-lessened face is makeup-free, and she's wearing a red silk tank top which, in contrast with the neon CHEZ JEANNETTE sign behind her head, makes a striking picture. I take a few photos and show them to her; she deletes three out of the four and hands the camera back to me, lighting a rolly from her crumpled pack of Fleur de Pays.

'It's cool here now,' she says. 'Crowds at night – there are bouncers.' Grég turns the music up loud, which I'm grateful for as I don't think I can string another sentence together. Nadine is saying something about Gaulier and someone from her class who's famous now and I'm glad just to nod, grateful we've taken our lives back up as though nothing happened. She asks if I want to come to Sceaux to watch the Gaulier soirée tomorrow night. I say I can't, I'm writing with Marie-France. The Gaulier school is focused on the individual performer, whereas Lecoq is more about collaborative creation. Their shows aren't as fun to watch. I don't tell her this, and it's true about Marie-France. I ask if she wants to come to the marionette show on Tuesday, the one I got the job for before the accident. She says no, dolls are creepy.

Two new glasses of wine appear on the table. Bad idea, I smile. Smart, says Nadine, it'll wake you up.

She suggests we move to the *terrasse* and Grég follows with our drinks. Early evening sun bathes our faces. She asks if I'm okay, must be weird to be back, and I say I'm fine, just a bit laggy. 'The sun will help,' she says, tilting her head back. The chicken salad arrives, delivered by a waiter with a slight amount of snobbery at the unconventional hour at which we're eating it, which Nadine ignores completely. 'Food will help you stay awake too,' she says, asking for another fork, salt and pepper and hot sauce – and the side of avocado? The salad is delicious – especially with the hot sauce – and has no toilet flavour. She describes her new, rude English teaching student and her recent reading at the English bookshop of a short story she wrote that she wants to turn into a play, or perhaps a book. I tell her I started playing with some old notes in Australia that might be a novel. 'What's it about?' she asks. 'Paris. I don't know. Remember how Adrien translated moths as "night butterflies"?' She tells me I should do a reading at the bookshop like she did, it was so much fun. 'One day,' I say. Right now I need to focus on the play, I've only got a few days in Paris to tie up the script with Marie-France before Portugal.

The Adrien-smell guy brushes past us and down the street in a cloud of scent.

'Oh yeah,' says Nadine, picking up on it.

'*Habit Rouge.*'

'You know he's engaged,' she says.

'Yes,' I tell her, jaw tight. Of course I know. In Dad's spare room on the other side of the world I harassed him as best I could, delirious on drugs, firing spite via email and text message. I was hung up on why he never came to visit me in the hospital. It was me who had ended it, well, my bike, turning me around on the way to his place and back towards the rental I'd just been offered on the rue de la Chine, but still. *You were my family in Paris*, I seethed at him. *It wasn't a scratch*. His mother, Séverine, never came either. I suspected they thought it was my own fault, which in my shock and delirium drove me insane. *Papillon fou*, he used to call me. Crazy butterfly.

'A Swedish chick,' Nadine continues. 'Caterina.'

Now I know her name. 'You've met her?' My stomach is a knot. I don't want to know about Adrien or Caterina, Nadine is too close to everything, I should have stayed at Harry's, but he's away and his weird flatmate is there. I could have stayed with Marie-France, but her boyfriend, and she's pregnant. Nadine is like a sister, I was always going to stay with her, but fuck, now I want to go home, I want to run back to Dad's, get under the scratchy covers and have him pat my head, run my bath, feed me schnitzels. Was I mad to come back so soon? Where am I?

Nadine feeds me more chicken salad and she's right, the food is telling my body I'm here, I'm awake. She is meeting some friends on the left bank for *apéro* and tells me I have to come. I don't want to, but she reinforces Kiki's rule about staying awake as late as possible. My neck throbs. She mounts her bike and I get a *Vélib*, feeling a moment of panic that subsides as I push off and muscle memory kicks in and we're sailing through the Marais like we always did, across the river to the café opposite Notre-Dame called Panis, which I always called Penis in my head. When I tell Nadine she wrinkles her nose and doesn't laugh. As she's chaining her bike outside the café I find ways to say Café Penis as many times as possible to break her, but she doesn't and finally says shut up with the Café Penis and when I ask her why she doesn't think it's funny she shrugs, it's just not. Now it's even funnier because she doesn't find it funny, and I tell her that but she's busy rolling a cigarette.

Café Penis is bustling with tourists eating dinner and Parisians drinking *apéro* and down the back near the bar are three pushed-together tables sticky with wine and beer and little bowls of stale popcorn. Nadine introduces me to an Irish guy with a moustache waxed into a curl, an English chick in a polka-dot dress, a French guy in a suit jacket and jeans, and the owner of the English bookshop's daughter, who I've met before – she's an actor and has the same agent as Nadine and I. She pulls a *tabouret* towards herself, patting it.

'I heard about your accident,' she says. 'I couldn't believe it – I still can't picture how it happened. You got your head caught in the door of the elevator?'

The waiter approaches and I order a *Seize*, and as the others talk I say no – well, not quite. The more she asks, the more the attention of the table turns my way and I feel my face go hot, the skin prickling around my scar. My hands tingle and my ankles clamp across each other beneath the *tabouret*. Nadine keeps talking loudly to the French guy in the jacket, perhaps to steer the conversation away from me, but his eyes have turned to me too, and though the bodies are in all different directions, they are listening.

'It's hard to explain,' I say.

'Sorry,' she says. 'You must hate talking about it.'

'No, it's fine. It feels like something that happened to someone else.'

There is no way to tell the story in a sound bite, though I had started to formulate a script in Australia after the barrage of questions from friends and family:

You fell down the elevator shaft?

The elevator fell?

You got your head trapped in an elevator?

The elevator closed on your head?

All eyes are on me now. I take a swig of beer, smile, dissociate, and repeat the script with a light, conversational air, though I'm burning with shame. Thank God for the acting training.

JAYNE:
You know the old buildings here with the lifts in the middle of
the staircases without protective enclosures around them?
(*nods, murmurs*)
Well, it was January, Paris was dark. My friend Sophie lives in
a 1930s building in the 20th and the lights were dim and the lift
moved up and down in total silence, a finger's breadth from the
banister – you could touch it. The protective barrier came just up
to banister height, which was low, and I'm tall, plus I was wearing
heels. Sophie's four-year-old daughter Lou called me from
below – we were playing a game of hide-and-seek. I was excited
to see her after a lonely winter breaking up with my fiancé. I was
calling to her – 'Lou!' And she was calling – 'Jaa-yne!'
To help her see me I leant slightly over the rail –
(*she illustrates the angle of the banister with her forearm and
moves her head over as if to look down*)
I could see Lou's face below
(*she puts her other hand above her head as if to show the
descending elevator*)
and I didn't realise that I had put my head in the path of the
descending elevator.

ENGLISH CHICK:
(*hand over mouth*)
Oh my god.

MOUSTACHE GUY:
Woah.

JAYNE:
Luckily the lift stopped and I managed to pull my head out from
beneath.

NADINE:
A miracle.

ENGLISH CHICK:
I feel sick.

THE BOOKSELLER'S DAUGHTER:
How did the lift stop?

JAYNE:
I don't actually know.

FRENCH GUY:
(*shaking his head*)
Always so many accidents in Paris in these old buildings.

THE BOOKSELLER'S DAUGHTER:
Unbelievable.

ENGLISH CHICK:
Then what happened?

JAYNE:
I don't know exactly – I blacked out and fell down the staircase.

ENGLISH CHICK:
But – you pulled your head out?

JAYNE:
Yes, but I don't remember any of it. I came to on the stairwell
after I fell down a flight of stairs.

THE BOOKSELLER'S DAUGHTER:
But you were okay.

JAYNE:
Yes. Well, kind of. I was lucky. They didn't realise until later that
I'd broken my cervical spine – my neck.

NADINE:
They put her in a soft collar to carry her to the hospital. A soft
collar! If she'd moved her head in any way she could have died or
been paralysed. Sorry Jaynie. Is this —

JAYNE:
It's fine! I'm just glad to have survived. I just had some broken
bones in my face and the neck fracture which they didn't even
have to operate on —

NADINE:
— because she was young and so fit from all the acrobatics
at Lecoq —

MOUSTACHE GUY:
All that falling training.

THE BOOKSELLER'S DAUGHTER:
Was there any other damage?

JAYNE:
Not really. I was lucky to keep my ear and there's this major
artery there, the carotid artery, that can be fatal … and I had this
amazing surgeon that stitched up my face with thousands of the
tiniest stitches.

MOUSTACHE GUY:
And what did they do about your neck?

JAYNE:
They put me in this new kind of brace thing – a *corset minerve*
it's called.

NADINE:
Like a robot contraption, she was suffocating.

JAYNE:
It was okay, I got used to it —

THE BOOKSELLER'S DAUGHTER:
In England they put bolts in your head – you know,
with the poles, the scaffolding —

NADINE:
Australia, too.

ENGLISH CHICK:
You were in rehab?

JAYNE:
I would have been, but my sister who's a nurse came and took
me back to Australia to recover with my dad in his cottage by the
sea. I've literally just arrived back.

NADINE:
(*patting Jayne's arm*)
She's recovered amazingly.

ENGLISH CHICK:
Are you okay now? Do you have pain?

THE BOOKSELLER'S DAUGHTER:
You can barely see the scars.

FRENCH GUY:
Why did you come back?

I tell them about the play and they all say they'll come when it's on in Paris and break off into smaller conversations. My throat feels tight and my head won't stay still. The sounds of the restaurant are loud in my ears but strangely muted at the same time, and my eyes keep fixing on the reverberations of light from the streetlamp outside. I am cool, so cool, all good, smiling, laughing at Nadine who is mimicking her rude student; my body feels like it's moving in the way you feel when you get off a boat, the darkening street outside is the deck of a ship, my head is in the sky, on the stairwell, asleep, in the sea.

'I am so jetlagged, Nadine,' I whisper after an appropriate amount of time has passed after the accident story that my departure won't seem dramatic. 'I have to go.'

'Don't go!'

'I need to go, I have that vertigo jetlag feeling that I'm going to black out right here, in the popcorn.'

'Will you be okay to ride by yourself?'

'Of course.'

'Okay, but you'll need to let me in later …'

'I'll leave the key under the mat, I fear I'll be unwakeable.'

'Okay, good idea.' She closes my hand around the key, with her warm, slightly sticky hand, and gives me a serious look. 'Ride safe.'

There's only one *Vélib* left and a young guy and I approach the stand at the same time. He steps aside in an unusually chivalrous move – *Vélibs* are dog-eat-dog. Perhaps he can see I'm about to collapse into a pile of dust.

Merci.

De rien.

He walks away lighting a cigarette. I get on the bike and push off slowly, Paris swirling around me in a dusky haze. Halfway across the Pont du Châtelet I stop to breathe and wait for the world to stop spinning. Out past Notre-Dame the lights are on, the sun shooting a final pink dart through the night sky. I try to remember the moment at 22, when down there on the riverbank I first saw the view for myself. The flash of independence I got in that moment had stayed with me; the feeling that I didn't need to be with someone else to truly experience something, that the world could exist entirely within me. It was that moment that had led me back here after Mum died, looking for that feeling again, of being whole while entirely alone.

Someone laughs. I turn around, a woman my age runs to catch up with her boyfriend. She wasn't laughing at me. Maybe it was me laughing at me. The Conciergerie looms over the river, its ghoulish facade containing the ghost of Marie-Antoinette waiting her turn at the guillotine. I've never been able to look at those conical towers without seeing her in there in her nightgown with her hair chopped off, sitting by a candle, writing her last letter. Perhaps I saw that in a documentary. I wonder what it feels like knowing you're going to get your head cut off. I'm grateful that if mine had been I wouldn't have seen it coming.

I ride off towards the Marais. Ghosts everywhere. Adrien in the Place du Châtelet kissing me in the snow, Kiki laughing in bars along the rue de Rivoli, Nadine dancing in dress shops, Marie-France leaning from her old window in the rue de Poitou, Harry skateboarding in République, my student friends picnicking on the cobblestoned edges of the canal. Ghosts from the accident, the flashes of light, the stairwell, the purple feeling in the back of the ambulance, the smell of sulphur, the sensation of my own face flesh being peeled back to touch itself, the ambulance lights strobing the walls of someone else's party, me at the party wondering who's in the ambulance and what happened to them.

Nadine's building looms over the murky canal, the facade dark and silent and ugly. It's allowed to be with those views. Who cares what something looks like, as long as it's looking *at* something beautiful? That thought comforted me when my face was bad and I thought my body was done for.

I fumble in my pocket for Nadine's key and pull out something triangular, grey and plastic. My head is quicksand; I stand staring at the strange yet familiar object. Giddy, it occurs to me what the object is. It's come all the way from Australia.

⁓

Nadine doesn't know about M. I haven't made a point of telling her and it's not like it would come up – *oh, by the way, since your monumental breakup, near beheading and recovery in a neck brace at your dad's, meet anyone?* Anyway, it's not like I *met* someone. I just met someone.

Nadine is snoring. I leave a note saying I've gone out for pastries, which is half true. I'm not sure why I'm half lying. I don't have words for M yet.

He is kind on the phone, and laughs at me calling it a plucker, saying it's not important at all, he has dozens of *plectrums*, none are special. I keep waiting for him to sigh, say *merde*, tell me to be more mindful, call me *papillon fou*. He says his plane leaves for Portugal on Friday week, right after the final gig with his band. He asks about my flight, Nadine, what it's like to be back in my old neighbourhood, what my plans are for the day, describe where I'm sitting. I tell him I don't think I've ever seen the canal this early, Chez Prune isn't open, the street sweepers are out, the sky is clear, it's going to be a pretty day. I love the smell of Paris in early summer, the mix of pollution and pollen. I ask where he is right now – he describes the servo on High Street, some guy filling up his car with the window down and Metallica blaring, the smell of old sausage rolls. The call cuts out and he messages to say *talk soon*. I try to imagine him here on the canal and can't.

Du Pain et des Idées is shut – damn, I forgot they close on Saturdays. The most popular boulangerie in the neighbourhood and they shut on weekends, *la vie est belle*. I have to go to the one on the rue du Château-d'Eau, which Nadine likes better anyway, their *pain au chocolat* more traditional and soggy with butter. She eats just the passage where the chocolate lies, and a bit of the pastry around it, leaving the flaky outer bits sitting on the paper. She has always done this. I asked her once if it was a dietary thing. She didn't answer but went on talking about the other thing she was talking about, as she always does when I annoy her.

There is a queue around the corner and up the rue du Château-d'Eau. My neck is killing me. Nadine's lumpy *oreiller* wasn't enough on the futon mattress on the floor; it hurt less with her winter jumper folded up on top, and sleeping in my scarf, but still. When my neck is bad I can't help thinking of the story my sister Kate told me about a man who has a head-on collision on the highway. He crawls from the wreckage, the sole survivor, and manages to walk to a nearby house. 'There's been an accident,' he tells the person at the door. 'Where?' they ask. 'Over there,' says the man, turning his head to indicate. And he falls down dead. He had a C2 fracture, non-displaced, just like mine. If he'd kept his head forward, he'd probably have been fine.

I pull the scarf tighter as I wait in the queue, grateful to have an appointment with Bérénice the *kinésithérapeute* before Portugal. I think she translates as physio but she's far stranger than that. I've missed her. All the stuff I've put in place here: health card, bank card, phone, *carte de séjour, kiné*. Piles and piles of paperwork. I'd stay here forever simply because of all the hard work it took to get set up.

The queue is stuck. A ray of sun is baking the top of my head. As I put my hand up to cover the part in my hair a drop of water hits the back of my hand, which gives me a shock. I step back. A woman on the fourth floor is watering her basil plant. She catches my eye and disappears behind her rusty balcony.

How many people die each year by falling pot plant? I would really like to know. I can see dozens up there, proud on their balconies. With age, weather, time, who knows, at some point they could drop. How many per year? Is there a list at the *commissariat*? Would they show me? The queue is still not moving. The drips are creating a small pool on the concrete. A man approaching the queue stops and tousles his hair, looks up, huffs. Are there laws around pot plants, regulations on spacing, height? Are you supposed to strap them in? I saw Séverine do that once – replace an old strap that was fraying. Do straps break, gusts knock, do old pots suddenly give way for no reason at all?

What a coincidence to be that person below. If only he'd left the office a second later/earlier/hadn't taken the boulevard, if only he hadn't stopped to buy a *pain au chocolat*.

We shuffle forward a few inches. Sitting ducks for a pot plant. Small, large, terracotta, worn. A long plastic tub of geraniums – the slut of the window box, Kiki would say. I like geraniums, they're more of a nanna plant to me than a slut. They were the only things that would survive on my small balcony in the Récollets, colour all year round. Adrien stubbed *clopes* in their dirt and still they survived. I was never in danger of killing anyone by pot plant in the Récollets; my window looked out over the park, and below was a cobblestone driveway locked off to the public. I think I would be afraid, on a narrow street like here on the rue du Chateau-d'Eau, that my plant would fall on someone, even if it was well-secured. In the rue de la Chine I had two window boxes and a small ledge outside the kitchenette where I put cheeses. In the window boxes I planted a geranium and some roses and I didn't tie the pots in, I never thought of it. My flat was on the first floor anyway, so I don't think the pots could have killed anyone, unless the entire balcony fell off. Has anyone's balcony ever fallen off? If the cheeses fell they wouldn't have harmed anyone. Though now I think of it, frozen in winter, a hard cheese, say, like a *comté*, could cause a nasty concussion. Getting killed by falling brie, now that would be a story.

At the counter, finally. The change machine was *en panne*. For the life of me I can't understand these machines that take your cash and give you change while the lady is right there. They always jam, there's always a problem, and seriously, is it that hard to put the money through the till? Is it a hygiene thing? Or an accuracy thing? It comes across like the boulangerie owner doesn't trust the staff to handle cash. It feels inhuman, and quite un-French. Though as soon as I think that I then think it's very French. Everything you say about the French is always true in its exact opposite. I suppose you could say that about most cultures. I suppose I shouldn't generalise.

Back at Nadine's the sun is shining across her mattress in a stripe and her quilt smells good, that sisterly smell of time and old shampoo.

We lie in the stripe and she doesn't bring up the accident, or Adrien, and I'm grateful to talk about current things like the play and her English students and the new Italian restaurant on the rue Marie-et-Louise and the upcoming summer *vide-grenier* on the Place Sainte-Marthe, my favourite, which I'll miss. She has a new boyfriend, a French guy called Didier, and I laugh because the guy in French textbooks in school was always called Didier and I never thought anyone would actually be called that. She smiles when I say this, although she doesn't find it funny. It's so hard not to needle her. I resist asking, Does he wear a beret? Does he know *où est la piscine?* Does he like the summertime?

My things look at home here. The stained red velvet chair I bought from the *marché aux puces* with Kiki that made me feel shabby-regal in my spartan room in the Récollets. I can see Adrien sitting on it right now, naked, smoking. His tea towel I stole. The handmade vase Séverine gave me for my 30th that lived next to my bed in the rue de la Chine. My things assimilate naturally into Nadine's environment with all the random objects she's gathered from *brocantes* and *vide-greniers* and the *puces*. She has an innate honing device that leads her consistently to gems. Like Kiki, she can spot the potential in things and her feelings about them are instantly laser-clear. Perhaps that's why I don't want to mention M just yet. I'm not sure what she might say.

I got to know Nadine better after school was over. Her eccentricities had kept me at a distance at first. For example, she is a long-orderer. And she sends things back – wine, meals, coffee – several times if necessary. And she always wants to move seats mid-meal to be in the better spot. For someone as afraid of offending waiters as I am this was a challenge, but over time I came to realise she was just incredibly motivated to make the most out of every moment. She wasn't desperate like I was to become French, to disappear into the culture, and of course they liked her and found me a suck and a fake. And there you'd be, in the perfect place, the one blinding ray of winter sunshine in the whole of Paris shining across your table, and you're eating a burger with the sauce from the steak dish in it, or drinking a *Perrier rondelle* with <u>three</u> slices of lemon, or the perfect glass of wine she accepted on the fourth go, and her hair is shining in the sun, her water fizzing into the sky (extra ice please), and she has read something fascinating and she just landed an ad for *dentifrice* and she is content like a cat. She isn't afraid to ask for what she wants. She knows who she is and what she likes, and she doesn't like poopoo jokes. She likes me despite this.

I remember her at my hospital bed, warm hand on mine. I remember it like a film. The girl in the bed looks like the elephant man, in a swollen state of shock.

JAYNE:

Do I look like a freak?

NADINE:

No. Just like you've been in a very bad car accident.

Flowers were forbidden but the ones she brought were grandiose – from her favourite guy on the rue Grange-aux-Belles who sleeps up on a ledge in his shop. Winter wildflowers in powder blues, whites and yellows. I can only imagine how long it took her to choose them, have him perfectly wrap them – *non, pas ce ruban-là – celui-là, le violet – nononon, on recommence* … There was no way these flowers weren't staying in my room, and my darling nurse Noémie, looking in Nadine's determined face, didn't put up a fight. She put them on the top of a cupboard where I could see them if I squinted hard enough.

Nadine faded in and out with the injections of liquid love in my thighs, the sweet pinch that kept me in fairyland. She was there the day I was fitted with the *corset minerve*, which I nicknamed the Cage. It was like being inserted into my own personal prison, with no air between my flesh and the bars. I was weaned brutally off the Love. I wanted to die then, it was worse than the pain, this nausea, this wanting to throw off my own body. Nadine sat beside me as I lay in the shadows. She knew not to touch me and not to speak. I loved her more than ever then, for her staying, her stillness, her silence, her ability to listen to me though I wasn't speaking. I did have family in Paris, other than Adrien and Séverine.

We lie around all morning on her quilt eating the pastries. She eats three chocolate middles and talks about Didier, the new yoga school she's discovered in the rue du Faubourg-Poissonnière, the ridiculous auditions Daphné Papps, our agent, has sent her to. She asks if I've told her I'm back and I say no, I'm not back yet, and also I'm not sure about my acting future. There's a lot of voiceover work around now, Nadine tells me, doing audio books and radio ads in French with the 'leetle English touch'. It's fashionable. She asks about Portugal and whether I feel comfortable directing, and I tell her of course not, I'd much rather be performing, but I can't be in a situation where I might be bumped. The doctors say I need to avoid unpredictable physical activities for at least the next six months, and acting is the most unpredictable physical activity there is – apart from sex perhaps. I never know what my body might do in either situation, so both are out of the question right now, though my libido hasn't been affected by the accident, *au contraire*. Regular orgasms, I've been telling myself, will heal my bones faster.

Nadine does not want to know about this. She is very interested, however, in the things I don't want to talk about, like if I feel strong enough to be back in the theatre, where I will live once the play is over, whether I'll go back to teaching the students I had before the accident, if I'll study again, how I'll make money ... I don't want to think about the future, I don't want to *think*. I keep having flashbacks to the separation from Dad at the airport, the tearing feeling of being a toddler sent off to school too early. Nadine presses more and more into the wounds, requiring more detail, not satisfied with my rote responses or attempts to shrug something off.

'How are you going to go with that gang in Portugal?'

'Fine,' I tell her, though I know what she's getting at. We're not used to the traditional writer-director-actor structure, at Lecoq we always collaborated and Nadine knows all about Dublin and the show Tez and I developed using a script of mine called *The Cherry Dress*, a piece about two mad sisters whose mother had died. Sort of *Grey Gardens* but two young women. We worked off my writing, but devised a mostly physical piece around it, which actually made the script even more personal and somehow even more my writing. When a local radio interviewer asked who wrote the piece, Tez had responded 'the two of us'. This had made me furious. She hadn't understood the work behind the writing, or the way my words had informed our physical piece.

I tell Nadine that after Marie-France asked me to direct the play, I made every member of the group confirm before I came that I was to be credited as director and writer, and that all final decisions would be mine.

'What about the script? Are you going Beckett on it?'

I laugh. 'I still want to give them room to move.' Not like in *Happy Days*, every gesture marked— "*Another heavenly day!*" Pause. *Smile. Look at bag. Look up.*

'No,' she insists. 'No room to move.'

'We're from Lecoq.' I say. 'They will stab me if I try to dictate.'

'Go Franco on that shit. They'll eat you alive.'

'It'll be fine, Marie-France is working on the script with me.'

Nadine is not convinced but senses subject closed and turns her questioning to my recovery at Dad's. Her apartment feels wonky, like it might fall off its perch. 'I'm *so* jetlagged,' I say, but she continues to press. My head won't stay still, it's driving me crazy, and my heart keeps speeding up and slowing down, my stomach churning. Memories of the accident are returning with the smell of the wood in her floors, the detergent in her towels, the damp funk of the *canivaux* running below her building, up through Belleville past the Père Lachaise to the rue Pelleport, to that dark stairwell on the night of January 18.

As Nadine goes to ask another question she checks her watch and jumps up. Whoops! – Going to be late late late.

I fall back in the sheets and close my eyes, grateful for the silence.

> I'm on the stairwell
> Flying out over it in slow motion
> Something cold on my neck

I wake with a start. My heart pounds, my head is a brick.

Breathe.

In for four, hold for seven, out for eight.
In for four, hold for seven, out for eight ...

Paris.
Nadine's.
Saturday.

I think I'll be falling down that staircase forever.

Nadine's lampshade, full of dead insects. My neck so stiff I can barely move it. 4 pm. The panic subsides. I lie and touch the right side of my face. The numbness beneath the scars, they say, is permanent. Dead skin, dead face. *Flattened affect.* Difficult to act with a face that's half numb. Nobody seems able to tell, and I can't notice when I look in the mirror. Strange to see one thing and feel another thing. Nadine has a small bar fridge. One egg and an old *bobun*, noodles floating in a bowl of scum. The sun is bright. My phone beeps. Three messages.

Marie-France: come at 17h

Harry: back 2nite, Carillon 2morro

M: *A square erupted, taking in live ballet move (9)*

Arabesque. Such a pretty word. It takes me only ten minutes to solve. I'm astonished my brain worked so fast, let alone at all. It's easier when you have no expectation of yourself. Like, when you're drunk. Your brain softens and you can see it quicker. M agrees with this, but he also thinks sharpness does help. I say a mix of both – which is why we're better at it together.

I text him the answer and he replies *Pas mal! Off to sleep now. M x.*
He knows how to kiss by text.

Nadine's tap water has white scum on it. She drinks it straight from the tap. Nadine is fussy over certain things, like the amount of *mousse* on her coffee, but not chemical flakes on her water. Her shower is plonked in a corner on top of the carpet: a plastic cubicle like the one I had in my *chambre de bonne* when I was an au pair. I used to piss in it as I had no toilet of my own. I try not to piss in Nadine's shower but it feels homely. My aim is excellent. Nadine might die if she knew I pissed in her shower, but I can't be sure. I can never tell how she will react to something, only that it will be extreme. She might kick me onto the street, quite seriously, neck and all. I let the water trickle into my mouth – if it enters me in droplets I can forget the calcification. Her towel is soft, I sigh loud into it, never to take showers for granted again. Nadine has no food or stove but she has a glittering array of perfume bottles on her plastic sink: Annick Goutal, Diptyque, Carthusia. My favourite is *Ce Soir ou Jamais* – Tonight or Never – with a crinkled gold ribbon around the neck. I like the name better than the scent, though it smells amazing on Nadine. Annick Goutal has the best names for her perfumes – Tonight or Never, *Un Matin d'Orage* (Stormy Morning), *Petite Chérie* (Little Sweety). Marie-France sent a bottle of *Petite Chérie* to me in Australia, and at first I thought I'd never wear it, I was not a little sweety. But the smell of it was like emerging from a shower of flowers, and especially in those funky first weeks when I couldn't take a shower it made me feel like a human being. I treasure it now – though it reminds me of that time, it seems to change with my evolution. When I was sick it smelt like fields. When I was dazed it smelt like presence. On the plane back to Paris it smelt like promise. I spray on Carthusia which smells like thief. And reminds me of something. The first day Nadine came to the Hôpital de la Salpêtrière she brought me a little roll-on stick filled with lavender and orange oil. 'To make the hospital smells go away.' She rolled it on the inside of my wrist and brought my wrist up to my nose. At that point I couldn't have deciphered a hospital smell from a flower bed and couldn't have cared less either way, but she left the vial next to my bed and as my awareness returned I clung to it, the nurses having to forcibly uncurl my fist and remove the stick to wash my hand, replacing it afterwards. I sniffed that thing like it was life itself. Life beyond that bed.

I sniffed the little stick all the way back to Australia in the plane. It helped me ignore the pain of sitting upright in the brace and the little turd behind me kicking the seat all the way to Dubai. I sniffed it in the bed at Dad's, where it was a reminder of Paris, my former life, the hospital. It made what had happened seem real. The smell grew as my senses returned until one day it was so intense it made me violently ill. I think the stick went in the bin the same day as the Cage, the oil inside having long dried up. Now I regret throwing it out. I regret throwing the Cage out too – I knew as I was doing it I would regret it, but it seemed like a ceremonial necessity at the time. Now it's lost research. And though part of me wants to forget everything about that experience, another part tells me to keep it close, every little detail.

Marie-France lives on the third floor and she has a lift. It fits two people and is fully enclosed. People keep asking if I'm scared of lifts now, they say, 'Bet you'll never take a lift again.' But it wasn't the lift that was the problem in Sophie's building, it was the stairwell. And the fact that the lift went up and down right in the middle there, chopping your bits off. Watching *Three Colours: Blue* in Australia with M, I froze when Juliette Binoche walked up a stairwell as the lift passed her, free and unenclosed, just as mine had. Standing here now on the ground floor I shouldn't feel fear, but I do. I think it's the idea of putting myself in the hands of a machine I have no control over. I've lost faith in moving objects.

My legs take me up to Marie-France's door. She opens it and stands smiling for a moment before reaching out her arms. '*On peut?*' We hug. I can feel she is scared of breaking me. When we step back she looks at my face, saying, 'Oh, Jayne,' and how happy she is to see me and oh how afraid she was and oh how much better I look than the last time she saw me, but *oh la la, si maigre.*

Her boyfriend isn't there and she has a little bump. It's so cute on her fragile frame. I want to rub it and she lets me, guiding my hand with her soft, slender fingers. She can't stop eating she says, so we sit at her kitchen table and she begins hoovering charcuterie. 'Are you supposed to be eating that?' I ask, and she grins at me, mouth full of ham. Even that looks delicate. She can't help it, she says, and if the baby wants bresaola what right does she have to say no. I can't believe she's pregnant, I tell her, it feels so *adult*. She looks confused by what I'm saying and I realise how natural it is to her that she has a little baby inside her, how normal it is that she's doubling. Her life doesn't seem to have changed at all. She doesn't appear to be encumbered by being pregnant, except for the bodily demands. She has to pee every five minutes, she says, moving towards the bathroom. And more. She may be a while.

I'm glad, because I want to poke around her flat. I love Marie-France's flat more than any place on earth. It's a small *deux pièces* on the rue Saint-Sabin, but *bien aménagé*. That means that everything is in the right place, the space is cleverly used. Is her place so lovely because of her, or was it like that from the start? There is the most beautiful light in the mornings from the left, and in the evenings from the right, and she has a little balcony that looks out over the shabby, homely street and its laundromat and *épicerie* and mix of life below. Her main room is painted a chalky greenish blue and everything inside has meaning – either old pieces from the country house she grew up in or things she's collected in the street or in old shops and new shops, with mirrors on tables and chests with vases on them and plants that are alive dotted about. On her balcony is an array of pots of all different sizes and colours, not strapped in, but they seem reasonably secure. Her bedroom is black with an antique painting of the moon and old maps and a Chinese screen with clothes flung over it, and there's a small balcony in this room too, with just a planter box full of a pretty white flower. No geraniums. The windows are flung open and I want to lie on her bed but it feels less mine now there's a baby and a boyfriend.

I was often here during school, sprawled out, making clown costumes or masks, the two of us smearing vaseline and *papier mâché* over each other's faces and trying not to laugh and crack the mould, taking the white expressionless forms once they'd dried and placing them on her table, marvelling at their lifelessness, life only appearing once we put them on. Marie-France's body could make any mask beautiful. I hated her in first year at school because she had such a natural ability to move and be *juste* and was so perfectly Parisian with her neat dark hair and thin body and no pimples. And she was nice. I wanted to knife her. I made her put on my *papier mâché* mask because it was lumpy and shit, and she brought it *grace*. That was a body. A Lecoq body. Now I think of it, our whole experience was about taking our bodies and making them our faces. Instead of expressing ourselves through our faces and minds, we were taught to speak with our bodies. I remember trying so hard as a younger actress to find the emotions in my head, searching for ways to be able to truthfully convey intent and feeling, to *be natural*, to *truly* laugh, to cry. I'll never forget a visiting Russian director – an expert in Meyerhold's biomechanics – yelling at us to stop what we were doing. He turned his back, hunched his body over and started to cry, his body heaving and shaking. With his back turned, voice choked, he called out: 'What am I doing?' We looked at each other. 'Crying,' dared one of the actors. The director slowly turned to us with a devilish smile.

He had been laughing the whole time.

'The actor is always laughing,' he said. 'It is the audience that is crying.'

I wonder how you work from your body when it's not working properly. I wonder how you write without being stuck in your head. My neck throbs, the place between the two. I rub it beneath the scarf and pick up the copy of *Le Corps Poétique* next to her bed, Jacques Lecoq's most famous book. Perhaps she's re-reading it, as I have recently. Looking for answers. Looking for how to direct a play. How to be truthful. How to be. In English it's called *The Moving Body*, which always seems such a sad translation to me; why can't we have *The Poetic Body*? My body doesn't feel poetic. Actually yes it does: an epic poem that is difficult to understand, impossible to follow. Her *Lettre à mes élèves,*

the small, elegantly bound document we all received on our last day of
school, is wedged into the book. I open it and Jacques Lecoq talks to me
from the grave:

Que faites-vous maintenant?
C'est après cinq ans que vous réaliserez ce que vous avez fait à l'école.
Où êtes-vous?

What are you doing now?
After five years you'll begin to understand what you did at school.
Where are you?

Hello Jacques, I am nowhere really, but alive. Guess what? I'm doing
what you said and making my own play, not just going off and being part
of someone else's work. Are you proud of me, Jacques? Is it because it's
only been one year that all I've learnt is a blur?

A polaroid of our class in *bouffon* costumes is stuck to the mirror
on Marie-France's dresser, along with an ultrasound image of her baby
and a library card. In the final year we spent an entire weekend in this
room sewing our *bouffon* costumes, listening to old *chansons françaises*
on her record player. The *bouffon* is a character that comes up from hell,
and because she is an alien she can say and do whatever she likes and
we will laugh and forgive her, as we would a child or a foreigner or my
slightly racist nan. If her body wasn't so ridiculous and deformed we
would think of her as evil. She has got to be unrecognisable as human.
In the art studio at school we drew our *bouffons*, mine was a triumphant
woman with boobs for eyes and a bulbous, back-to-front body wearing
a beauty pageant sash: MISS STRAYA. We then had to make the bodies
out of stretchy white cloth stuffed with cushion-filler. A sort of body-
mask. Marie-France and I gathered our materials from the Marché
Saint-Pierre then came back to her flat to work, stuffing and stitching
and disappearing intermittently into her bedroom to look in her mirror.
I wanted a 'gunt', which I couldn't explain to Marie-France. A gut-
cunt. Gut-front. 'A front bum,' I said. '*Derrière arrière?* Front *derrière?*'

She didn't get it – she'd probably never seen one. Finally, I stood on her table and she made the last few stitches and there I was – a bulging hyper-female beauty queen with cannon tits, a bulging twat and front wedgie. I loved myself! Sweating like a madwoman I got out of my suit and helped Marie-France into hers. I couldn't imagine what it would look like; her drawing was quite demure, just a fat person basically. But as she pulled it on, I saw she had made a giant dick with a fat knob on the end, the same height as herself, which she attached to the front of her fat suit. She placed a rope around the foreskin and held it like the reins of a horse, shouting '*Allez allez!*' as she rode it around the room. I stood in shock, more in love with her than ever.

All these trinkets. A green glass cloche with a dried flower beneath it. A candle that smells like gardenia flowers, Mum's favourite. A painted ashtray with a gold part to hold the cigarette. I can't imagine her boyfriend here, Hakim, the tall corporate guy from her home town near Bordeaux. He has kept his place in Levallois, she told me – it's closer to his work, and there's no way she's moving out there.

At the sound of Marie-France's flush a surge of clarity rushes through me. I'm awake. I'm here.

She moans as she comes out and sits back at the table – her body is a *chantier*. A building site? My French hasn't waned as much as I thought it would, though she tells me I say some funny things, more *Anglo*. I'm suddenly starving and hack into the terrine and bread like it's my last meal, washing it down with rosé and ice cubes. Marie-France's mother has been driving her crazy, she says, hovering around, making her eat certain things, fussing. The thought of a mother still jolts me. The *concept* of mother. I already can't remember what that unconditional warmth feels like.

Marie-France is excited about Portugal, she says, to get away from her mother, but she's also afraid. I get it, I say. Well, I don't, actually, but I can understand that it will be weird to be in another country. Not that Portugal is far, and she can come back easily any time. Distances are different for Europeans. We are going to Portugal because Tez, who is now in our *compagnie*, got an arts grant from the council in her home town near Porto, for three weeks of rehearsals and a one-week production. Marie-France had already applied for a summer theatre festival in Paris and had been accepted and given a small amount of funding, so that had helped Tereza – we called her Tez – get the Portuguese grant. This, it seemed, was how things worked in the Arts: once someone gives you money, more people do. Marie-France and I had initially planned to extend the piece we made at school called *I'm Sorry, We Still Have Time*, but with the group we decided instead to extend a piece Tez, Faye, Meg and I had made in Tragedy about a woman who has a meltdown in a supermarket. The piece was a big hit in *autocours* and we performed it at the end of term *soirée* and it received raucous claps and beaming faces from the *profs*, sunshine as rare as gold. *C'est ÇA*. We smashed together text from Howard Barker, Sarah Kane and Christopher Durang to make a work about perfection and womanhood. My favourite moment was when the *coryphée*, the leader of the chorus who was played by me, began to fall apart, and half the chorus started to giggle while the other half broke into tears, and the laughter/tears built to a terrifying cacophony of female cries. It was wonderful, one of those moments in theatre that could never have life in any other form. It *was* life. I'd never thought of theatre's relationship with death before then. I realised that a moment of theatre, unlike other art forms, cannot be captured and reproduced in any way once it's passed. A live music show is the same, but you can listen to the album later. A recording of theatre is never the same, even dance retains a certain amount of its essence on a screen. Theatre is new every night, it startles and shocks – well it should, anyway. Anything can happen. The sets could fall, an actor could cough blood and die, lightning could strike and disintegrate the roof. You could pull your pants down. That last one has always plagued and taunted me during monologues. Because I *could*.

For the grant application I threw on the title 'Martha Goes to Market', which we all actually like. *Martha has massacred her family and would like to buy a tin of peaches in peace, if you don't mind.* It's an absurd, grotesque, tragicomic piece. There will be six performers: Élodie Paris, Faye Ohio, Meg London, Ana Spain, Tez Portugal and Marie-France

France. At Lecoq I remembered names according to their countries and it stuck, though I can surely let them go now there's not two Élodies. Marie-France will play *coryphée*, and the other five will play the vast, monstrous worlds inside a woman's head.

'What will it be like to play a murdering mother while you're pregnant?' I ask Marie-France.

She looks confused. 'Like acting.'

'You're not worried about it getting inside you?'

'Of course not! It's acting, remember, it's not real.'

Adrien left this annoying thing in my head about being careful what you let into yourself – roles and movies and ideas. When I watched the movie *Irreversible*, he warned me it would get inside me and stay there and I desperately wished I had listened to him. When I cried over my mother he would tell me not to let myself think that way, that she was fine and didn't like it when I cried. I said how do you know? He said he just did. He put that idea in me and that made me feel better, unless I did cry. But I cried less. And I tried to put better things inside me, but I also loved dark things. He said that was fine, but you had to have a method for getting rid of them afterwards, like after finishing a role. Meditation, walking, cleansing. I didn't know how to do those things. But the idea of being careful stayed with me, or at least aware. Marie-France screws up her nose as I am telling her this. Or, she says, you just move on.

She will leave for Portugal on Monday after her check-up. The others are already over there. I will fly in on Wednesday. It had been important to me to go the marionette show on Tuesday, though now I'm here I've changed my mind. I'd been so excited to get a role in that show, working with those delicate dolls in that dusty old theatre. But the theatre is in the 20th. The thought of setting foot anywhere near that part of Paris does strange things to my body: my pulse races and I feel like I'm going to faint. I wish Marie-France could come with me. Maybe Harry will. The idea of Harry at a marionette show makes me giggle inside my head.

I pull out my laptop and a printed copy of the script. Strange to be dealing in scripts, rather than just hitting the floorboards. Marie-France glances over the pages then puts her head in her hands.

'What's wrong?'

'*Cette ville ...*' she moans.

'What do you mean?'

'I can't believe what happened to you! This fucking city!'

'Oh, that.'

'You wouldn't be directing this thing, we'd be performing it together. It's weird you're directing. I'm glad, don't get me wrong, but you don't want to direct!'

'I know. I want to do cartwheels.'

She looks at me, eyes watery. 'Will you be able to do cartwheels again?'

In first year we 'learned' cartwheels. I remember being confused – *learning* cartwheels? As the teacher demonstrated putting one hand down, then the other, then landing on one foot, then the other, *main, main, pied, pied*, myself and the two other Australians in class simply did one. Marie-France was behind me. *Mais non!* I looked around. Most of my classmates were awkwardly putting down one hand after the other, trying to fling their bodies over. Marie-France looked more uncoordinated than I had ever seen her, begging me to help. It occurred to me that I had grown up in a country with a lot of physical space: doing a cartwheel was as natural as sneezing. To those from the high rises and concrete playgrounds of the rest of the world it was a complex acrobatic move.

'Of course I'll cartwheel,' I tell Marie-France. I don't know if I will.

'When I think of what happened ... I keep thinking of that little girl. Lou. Have you seen them yet?'

'No.'

'I saw them outside the hospital one day.'

'I don't remember seeing them in the hospital.'

She swallows. 'Perhaps they didn't come inside.' *Pause.* 'Oh, what are you going to do? I wonder if they've made the building safer, I can't —'

She senses she has said too much and stops to draw breath. 'I'm sorry, I'm so emotional right now. I'm just so glad you're okay!'

I reach over and hug her, my body still rigid like it's in the brace. She is careful not to squeeze me. I rub her back, feeling her hard little belly against mine.

'I'm happy to be directing. It will be fun. Weird but fun. You have to back me up, okay? You know Tez and Meg will want to do it their way.'

'I will. And then your friend M is coming to work with us!'

'Yeah, you'll love him.'

'Is he an old friend?'

'No, I actually met him at Dad's during my recovery.'

'A friend of your dad's?'

'No, a friend of Kiki's. You remember – my friend from the Cité des Arts. The painter.'

'Didn't she introduce you to Adrien?'

'Yep.'

'I meant to tell you, I saw him on the boulevard.'

'Oh. Did you say hello?'

'No, I mean in an ad for hairstylists.'

She hunts around for her phone and shows me a photo of a billboard with Adrien and two women posing. I laugh a bit. He looks pissed off. I think I remember when this was taken, after a tumultuous weekend at his mother's country house.

'I can't wait to meet M,' says Marie-France. 'Is he nice?'

⟋⟍⟍⟋

M *is* nice. I liked him the moment I met him. He and Kiki are old friends and when she decided to come down from Sydney to visit me, he was rehearsing on weekends at his band mate's holiday house just around the corner from my dad's, so she arranged to stay there. She brought him to visit one day without warning, which infuriated me. But it instantly didn't matter.

She called him M because he was so Melbourne, the Melbourne Musician, the MM, the M. And it was true, in his black t-shirt and dirty jeans he did look like he'd just rolled out of a perpetual all-night band venue. We sat in Dad's living room eating supermarket madeira cake. He looked funny in Gran's rocking chair, thin ankles crossed, comfortable as pie. He told Dad he'd just moved into a new place too, his own flat thanks to his day job in insurance for pensioners. Why are you telling me, Dad said, do I look like a pensioner? We all laughed. He was a pensioner. It was impressive that M was a struggling musician with his shit together enough to buy a place. He hated the job, he told us, but it meant he could eat while making the music he wanted to make. Dad said he'd worked all his life so now he could listen to the music he wanted to listen to, and put on an album, Jimmy Hendrix's blues. M noticed the cryptic crossword I was working on, a DA. In the main Melbourne newspaper, the cryptics have a different author for each day of the week, and Fridays are composed by someone called DA – Dick Arse I say, or Don't Attempt. DA is by far the hardest one to do, but the most creative and wild and revelatory and rewarding – even if you only solve two clues each week. M picked it up and said, 'Not bad!'

'You do the DA?' I asked.

'I try.'

'Have you ever finished one?'

'Not even close.'

He asked if he could take mine back to the band house with him, see if he could do some damage. On Sunday night the doorbell rang and I found the crossword on Dad's doorstep with a pink post-it: *Complete as much as possible and place under mat by Friday 6 pm.* The clues he answered were the ones I found most difficult and vice versa. Our minds worked in opposite ways, but if we pencilled our hunches in the margins, the other would knock it over the line. It took a few weeks, but we got that one out. A miracle. Dad put it on the fridge.

M started dropping in on the weekends and staying a bit, with that week's crossword, and books and films and music. One night he made Dad and I his Spaghetti Napoli. I started waiting for the sound of his shitbox Lily pulling into the driveway on a Friday night, her boot full of strategically chosen things to keep my mind alive while my body was dead. He didn't seem to notice the state I was in, never commented on the brace or my face and timed his questions with care. Kiki said I should kiss him, which was ridiculous and funny. She even said at one point I should sleep with him, claiming that instead of killing me it would heal me faster. She was nuts. His recent relationship had been as tempestuous as mine, and like me, he had sworn off them for good.

Besides, I was locked in the Cage, robot girl with the Frankenstein face. Frankenjayne. My hair had grown out weird because I'd had an ill-timed sharp fringe cut just before the accident. My legs were hairy, my skin sticky and pale, and the only things I could wear were track pants and button-down t-shirts: items I could take off myself without having to expose my tits to Dad, not that I wasn't past caring if Dad saw my tits, but it would have been awkward, I'm sure, for him. I was in an intimate relationship with my father. I stank, showering was difficult, my sense of smell was too sensitive to wear deodorant (anyway, why?), makeup would be weird. I had nothing to offer, and not only was I a fetid stick of human flesh, I was also engaged in heavy phone and internet warfare with Adrien, obsessed with making him pay for abandoning me in the hospital, and for already hooking up with someone else.

I would return to Paris once I was better and M was planning to move to New York, so we had the simple luxury of enjoying each other's company. An old-fashioned friendship. I liked him. There was something *still* about him. He took pauses when he spoke, and the thing that followed was always worth waiting for. It wasn't that he needed time to figure out what he was going to say, or indulged in lofty silences, he was just confident to take a space. He loved theatre and had worked on several plays as a musician. He liked Robert Wilson and Tom Waits and Fellini. He was curious about Lecoq. He asked to read my writing and I showed him a few short stories and the beginnings of the Paris novel, even the sex parts with Adrien, which he didn't find disgusting, even saying I should go further. He played his band's albums for Dad and me; post-grunge indie rock, melodic guitars, strings, driving drums. Dad didn't mind it, he said, but he preferred Deep Purple. I liked it – winding songs with dramatic middle sections and insistent outros that didn't care if they were too long to be played on the radio. Some of the songs were familiar from my university days. Now he had quit the band to pursue his own project and they were rehearsing their very last show. New York was next, where a few of his music friends had moved to start new bands. He wanted to put together his own instrumental band and tour there. I loved the new music he was creating, and he'd make playlists of the demos for me to listen to in my headphones. Sparse instrumentals using only his guitar – fingers scratching and pulling at single strings, the recording close and unaffected. *Juste*. That famous word from the Lecoq school drilled into us day after day, that felt impossible to find. The place, so fine, between too much and not enough.

We talked about everything; our parents, our projects, our relationships – there was nothing to lose, we knew this was a bubble in time before we went back to our lives. Eventually we talked about the accident and he carefully extracted the details, the lead-up, the night it happened, what happened after. I told him the entire story of moving to Paris after Mum died, the desire to leave anything familiar behind, the wild energy I'd felt through school and the days with Adrien, building to those dark weeks alone in the flat in the rue de la Chine, the ecstatic melancholy of it. How it all had culminated in that moment on the stairs where a disproportionate desire to see Lou's face had led me to lean over the banister. The cold feeling on the side of my head as it got trapped beneath the elevator, the rising, the roar in my ears before I blacked out. M listened patiently, intrigued that something like this could happen in such a modern place. He probed deeper – checking I didn't mind – trying to picture how the elevator could have come in contact with my head. It was a relief to be asked such detailed questions, as if he were validating that it happened and lifting it from a certain place in my psyche. I drew pictures for him, showing how you could easily touch the elevator box from the stairwell. He asked if I'd spoken with any lawyers after the accident and I said no, why, what would I say? His job in insurance was to constantly assess risk and fault and damages, and he just couldn't see how the accident could have been my fault. Unless I'd climbed up and deliberately stuck my head beneath the lift.

One Friday he came to visit and I wasn't there, I was in a hospital ward with three old dying ladies. The high levels of drugs I was on had led to excruciating stomach pain and a failing liver. A mistranslated French prescription. They put different drugs in me and pulled a curtain around so I couldn't see the women, only hear the gurgling and farting noises in the night. Dad brought me cryptics and a hopeful peanut-butter sandwich and sat beside me as I willed him to leave gently, without displacing the air particles around me and causing more pain. My arms were yellowed and bruised from blood-drawing, the smell of casserole was unbearable. I woke to doctors with clipboards hovering over me, marvelling at my brace. *Revolutionary.* Mavis in the next bed died, sounds of sobs and silences. I stared at the roof, begging the ants to leave my veins, wondering how easy it would be to get to the rooftop and throw myself off.

One night the curtain opened. It was M, in an ill-fitting suit. He had driven all the way from Melbourne after work, hours of traffic each way, just to say hi and bring a half-done crossword. Visiting hours were long over; the nurse gave us fifteen minutes. He sat beside me and told me it was fine not to speak. He told me about the shows he'd seen, and a book by Rilke he thought would be great research for my book, and a new song he'd written inspired by the coast, which he had put on an iPod for me to listen to with a new playlist. The nurse came back and he touched my shoulder, and left.

When I finally left the hospital he didn't come for a while, to let me recuperate. I missed him but was also glad he didn't come; I was adapting into a new life form. In the hospital I had insisted on ceasing all medication, which helped my liver repair but allowed me to feel the breaks in my neck and face with stunning clarity. The pain was something else, but it was good to feel exactly what was going on, to be aware of it, awake, no longer safe in a cocoon of drugs. Without the medication I could eat more and as I became accustomed to the pain I grew stronger, which in turn made me heal faster, and after some time I was able to take walks outside, to the beach, to Dad's rock to sit with him and watch the ships pass. One day, still in the Cage, I walked into the sea and fell blissfully beneath a wave.

The next time M returned I was sitting on the spare room bed with the Cage off, wearing a garish new dress Dad had bought me with flowers on it. He was nervous to approach me in case I turned, but I told him it was fine, the doctors said the bone had sufficiently healed. He sat next to me and slid his hand into mine. I squeezed it back.

'We need someone to do the sound and lights for the show in Portugal,' I told him.

He took only a few moments to say yes.

⌒

I wake with no clue where I am. My neck is worse. Nadine has left a note: *at marché, come down when u wake.* I get dressed and walk down to the Carillon, the corner bar that Nadine loves opposite the Alibert markets. Their terrace is lovely and their coffee terrible and in the evenings they have live music and DJs and you must never ever drink the punch on the bar, I still have no memory of what happened after that. Harry points to the glass jar with orange peel floating in it as I arrive, raising his eyebrows.

'Remember that?'

He hugs me and the bartender high-fives me, the guy we call Speed Queen for his untiring enthusiasm, never even dampened by Nadine's *exigeances*. Harry's arms are warm as ever.

'You look good,' he says. 'Skinny. I feel like I'm going to crush you.'

'I was anorexic,' I tell him as we sit down. 'That's the technical term they use in hospital, you know, when you're not eating. It's not just a psychological thing.'

He gives me a strange look.

'I.e., I didn't mean to be anorexic. I got sick. But let's not talk about that. I want to hear about Corsica. I want to hear about everything else but me.'

Harry has finally got his residency papers after living in Paris for over twenty years. He never bothered though he could have had them years ago – he went to high school here, his dad is a diplomat. He's more French than Australian, if you count the years he's lived here. Yet he still looks as Australian as if he's just stepped off a beach, with his wild blond hair, thinning up front now, tan, loose t-shirt and shorts. Harry helped me paint my walls in the rue de la Chine, and helped Kate move me out after the accident, redistributing my things to Nadine and his *cave*, arranging flights, paperwork. We kissed once, sort of, when I was fighting with Adrien, but the idea of being with an Australian at that time was abhorrent. I had left Australia to get lost, not hook up with my next-door neighbour.

Harry has a new girlfriend now, a Finnish chick called Hanne. He has just finished filming a new documentary about fish and will be spending every day of the next three months in an edit suite in the 15th, so he's taking in as much air as he can. He suggests a bike ride that afternoon. I say yes please, though I would rather spend the day in a soft, quiet box, with one of those neck holders with suction caps they use on trains in Japan, where your neck is always supported and you can sleep even while you're standing. I saw them once in a documentary. Nadine arrives from the market with her caddy sprouting celery and carrot tails and suggests we sit outside. She orders her coffee *sans mousse mais absolument zéro* and we wiggle our way amongst the bodies out in the sun to find the perfect spot, half in the shade, where Nadine can bake her face and Harry and I can sit under the awning. Our coffees arrive, hers the flat white I always want but no matter how much I say *sans mousse* there is always a tower of it that, rather than send back, I scrape with embarrassment onto the saucer and then search for a plant to tip it into so the waiter doesn't see. You'd have thought that, given the fact I also asked for a *crème sans mousse*, they might do mine the same.

'I don't like that Jean,' says Nadine, referring to the *primeurs* at the bottom of the market strip in front of us. 'I'm going to change to the guys up the top.' Jean has been at the markets forever, bringing his family every Sunday morning, dirt still beneath their nails. There is conjecture in our little group about whether they put the dirt there to seem more authentic. They speak with a country twang and have beautiful, overpriced produce that competes with the Laotian family's further up the strip; theirs has no dirt on it but is way cheaper.

I bought a bag of oranges once from the Laotians, and the look Jean gave me on my walk past his stall was enough to stop me doing it again.

It occurs to me that Harry never shops here at all. He doesn't do a weekly shop, he says, he just grabs bits and pieces as he wants them from the *primeurs* on the rue de Lancry. He mostly eats from the Lebanese shop, the Greek shop and the fish shop down there anyway. 'But your chicken curry!' I say. '*Primeurs*.'

Harry wants to hear about my recovery but the sun is so nice we all give up talking and stretch out in it. Nadine smokes, Harry drinks his beer, we listen to the people's conversations around us, the sound of the markets, children passing on *trottinettes*, the guy spruiking his roast chickens on the market strip.

'Do you plan to stay in Paris?' asks Harry eventually. 'After the play?'

'Of course. Where else would I go?'

'You mentioned New York in your email.'

'Oh, yeah, I thought I might go and check it out. I've got a wedding in LA early next year – Gabriella, remember Nadine my old friend from theatre school in Melbourne?'

'You want to move to New York?' says Nadine.

'No, but you know, you could work in theatre there, in your own language. Don't you ever think of it? Daphné would approve, she's always saying "Why ze fuck are you 'ere if you are Engleesh?"'

'But you love it here.'

'Yeah, well ...' I rub my temples. 'Anyway, we'll see after Portugal.'

'You'll stay,' she says.

'I know I will. I intend to. It was just a loose thing I'd been thinking about.'

'New York makes way more sense to me,' says Harry. 'But then I've never understood your Paris thing.'

Harry wheels my bike to Nadine's that afternoon and tears well in my eyes like being reunited with a best friend. I bought Betty from the dodgy brothers down the canal when I first moved to the Récollets. She's a nondescript Amsterdam, sure and true, and after being harboured by Harry all this time she looks curiously shinier than she ever did, with pumped-up tyres and her *guidon* pointing straight. I smooth her seat with my hands: the cracks in the vinyl are still there, created by my pumping butt, late for everything, flying through the streets hair streaming.

I give Harry a hug then we mount the bikes and he leads the way up the canal past the grey neighbourhoods of the 19th and over the *périphérique,* past the high-rises and stone houses and all the way to Rambouillet, into the forest. I'm glad we've come out this way where there are less people and little chance of being knocked. Harry seems to have sensed my fragility and chosen this route especially, one we've taken before but not for a long time.

In the forest we dump our bikes and go walking amongst the trees where the air is fresh and cool. Harry opens his backpack and takes out two beers and some chips.

'I love that you thought of this.'

'Always thinking beer-ahead.'

I prop myself up against a tree and he falls back in the grass. I unwind my winter scarf from around my neck to air out the sweat, feeling the air against my skin, which has gone soft from being hidden for so long. We sit for a while in silence, the beer making my head pleasantly woozy.

'Can I see your scar?' asks Harry.

I turn my face to show him.

'Man. But it's healed up well.'

'Yeah.'

'Adrien asked me to be his friend on MySpace.'

'Oh god. Did you?'

'Nah. I don't want him to see my music.'

'You have great taste in music!'

'No, I mean the music I *write*. I put it on there.'

'Oh, *that* music.'

'Shut up! It's good.'

'Yeah, it's excellent.'

He goes to wrestle me then catches himself.

'Ha! You can't bash me anymore.'

Adrien was feverishly jealous of Harry and it feels good to enjoy him without feeling I'm cheating on someone. It's taking far longer than I expected to peel Adrien from my soul. I ask Harry if his friend Michel's spare room got taken and it has, so I don't bother asking if M could stay there during the Paris run. He has a place sorted anyway, he's told me, but it would have been great to have him in the neighbourhood.

Harry doesn't want to come to the marionette show. We find a pond and throw rocks in it. He tells me I gave them a wicked fright, he's still haunted by it. I thank him for helping Kate move me out of the flat and for all the stuff he did. We wander back to our bikes and head towards Paris, chatting along the wider paths before we hit the narrow canal. He thinks I'm crazy for coming back: if he was me, he would have stayed at the beach. I tell him he's living the life that so many people dream of. He's not complaining, he says, but to be able to live close to nature, surf every day, who wouldn't want that? Plenty of Australians, I say. Living here is different to visiting, he says. I know, I say.

Harry has a film premiere to go to at 3 pm and invites me to go with him but I tell him I want to stay in the real world while I'm here. We pat each other's backs near Stalingrad and he takes off towards the Buttes Chaumont and I head back to the rue du Faubourg-Saint-Denis. A Kurdish sandwich. A cake called Divorce. A paper bag of *tomates cerises*, their rich tang reviving my insides. That familiar sense of home and also nowhereness envelops my body and leads me down the street and over the boulevard into the 2nd. Before I know it, I've arrived outside the métro Sentier. I enter the station with no purpose at all, like in the days when I was an au pair and would take random lines to no destination, jumping off at random stops and finding my way back again. Sentier is on the line 3 and goes in two directions – towards Gambetta in the 20th, my stop for the rue de la Chine, and Malesherbes, my first stop from when I lived in Paris as the au pair. Most recent memories at one end, most distant at the other. How funny that my legs brought me here. I head, of course, to the platform for Malesherbes – there is no way I'm going anywhere near Gambetta.

The carriage smells like home. A guy opposite me is reading Camus' *La Chute*. I read a lot of Camus when I was recuperating in Australia. *The Plague, The Myth of Sisyphus, A Happy Death*, his essay 'Reflections on the Guillotine'. I was curious to explore what would have happened if the descending lift had kept moving and taken my head. The book was mostly an argument against capital punishment but there was some great detail in there. Camus' dad went to watch the guillotining of a man who had committed a particularly grisly murder of a family with young kids. Monsieur Camus got up in the dark and crossed town to see justice served. He came home, rushed to his bed, lay down and spontaneously vomited. The decapitated, it became known, do not die immediately. A man called Languille, after decapitation, responded to the calling of his name. Another man, his head about to be put in the box with his separated body, looked up at the assistant with a look of supplication, as though asking forgiveness. The gory details of what happens to the body and the head after the event didn't bother me; on the contrary, I needed to know. Information was calming. I read about hangman's fractures, the mechanics of elevators, the history of Paris architecture, the science of the guillotine, poor Dr Guillotin, who was against capital punishment and, trying to find an alternative to the punishment of the day – burning at the stake, dismemberment, boiling – wanted to create a device that would inflict on the victim no more than a cold sensation on the neck. The machine, unfortunately, constructed by Antoine Louis, proved a more gruesome death than anyone could have imagined. They kept it anyway, and gave it the prettier name, La Guillotine.

The bigger the stories, the smaller mine felt. The bed was heavy with Dante and Kafka and Artaud and the existentialists and the surrealists and the nihilists and the absurdists and anyone who had been severely depressed, perplexed or mad. I looked up bizarre accidents, stupid deaths, hilarious near misses. Molière, who coughed blood and consequently died while on stage playing Argan the *Malade Imaginaire* – the fake invalid who pretends he's dying to find out how his wife truly feels about him. Aeschylus, killed by a tortoise dropped by an eagle who mistook his bald head for a rock. One poor actor doing a sex scene on a piano that was lowered into the room by a hydraulic motor which accidentally went up instead of down and squashed him on the roof in front of everyone.

Thinking of the onlookers was painful, almost as much as the person's death. It made me think about Sophie and Lou, what they must have seen on the night of my accident. What I had inflicted upon them. Walking up those stairs expecting to find me standing, smiling …

Isadora Duncan's accident felt closest to mine: an act of sublime enthusiasm and grave stupidity. Death by scarf: *Adieu, mes amis! Je vais à la gloire!* The train of silk flying out over the Riviera, the car wheel, *crunch*, flying Isadora. Some say her neck was broken by the tightening scarf, others that she died on impact with the road after being flung from the car. 'Affectations,' said Gertrude Stein, 'can be dangerous.' My accident wasn't the result of affectation, and it didn't result in death, but still, the story made me feel slightly less alone. I was looking for answers I suppose. Something, someone to relate to. Anyone who'd been through anything similar to me was dead. Extremely, horrifically, dead.

The Camus guy is getting off at Malesherbes too, and I follow him out of the clean-smelling station and up into the square I remember so strongly from my first days in Paris. How long ago nine years feels. How young was that 22-year-old girl with her living mother and her broken heart, getting kicked in the shins by a four-year-old who told her she was ugly and spoke bad French. The neighbourhood looks the same. I walk down the rue Cardinet to the place I lived with the Cansons and stop outside my old door and take a photo of myself to send to my sister Kate. She lived with me for a month in that room, eating tinned tuna stuffed in baguettes and listening to Massive Attack in cranked up earbuds.

I can just make out the window of my old *chambre de bonne* up on the 5th floor. It's propped open, someone is living in there – another au pair or slave to someone else's household, a cleaner, a nanny, a cook. The second floor where my employers, the Cansons, lived is as florid with greenery as ever, giant pots on the sturdy balcony that will never, ever fall. Down the street, the boulangerie is still there where the woman would serve me the burnt baguette, the little Proxi supermarket, the tall, clean Haussmanian buildings with their elegant stairwells and intricate lifts. I turn down towards the rue de Levis, which is as vibrant as I remember it, market stalls out the front of larger shops, a Monoprix, wine and cheese and flowers. I remember discovering this street for the first time, after thinking that Paris was only boulevards and monuments and manicured parks. The rue de Levis was the Paris I longed to know, bustling and messy and alive, with smiling faces and people calling out to you to buy things. I stop to buy a macaron and then I see him. Adrien.

An enlarged photo in a shop window. It's him with two women, the same image Marie-France had on her phone. His hair is slicked back with a small piece falling in his eyes, he's leaning forward on his knee, looking at me. *Tu ne m'aimes plus.* A smile I don't understand spreads across my face. The strangeness of it, his presence and yet his absence. I don't want to kill him at all.

⌒

Bérénice Bayeux's rooms are in an ugly cement building in the rue des Rondeaux, on the side of the Père Lachaise closest to the rue de la Chine. That's why the hospital set me up with her during my recovery. The thought of going there now makes my whole body clench, but if I cut through the Père Lachaise from the boulevard entrance down the bottom I should be able to avoid all association with my old life.

I decide to walk rather than ride or take the métro, it's overcast but there's a warm breeze. Down the canal and up the avenue de la République: forgot it's such a long way. Thank god I remembered to wear sneakers. I wore boots to Marie-France's and on the short walk from the *Vélib* stand to her place the impact of my soles on the pavement created a ricochet that went right up into my neck bone. After twenty-odd steps it became so painful I had to tiptoe up her stairs on my toes, my heels hanging over the back. The walk to Bérénice's is boring but the larger streets feel safer: there's less chance of being randomly knocked and cars are more likely to stop at crossings. Bizarre accidents play constantly in my mind – a pane of glass falling and slicing people's heads off, a bus squashing an old man, dogs crushed beneath bike wheels. Strangely, the images comfort me – it's as though if I see them first, they won't happen. At the gates of the cemetery I stop for a moment, relieved that all the people inside are already dead.

The guard wishes me *bonjour* and I attempt to carve a route through the cemetery I've never taken before, so as not to awaken any memories, but I come immediately to the tomb I stood crying beneath on Boxing Day like a pathetic little shit. I'd just spent Christmas Day on the floor in the dark, drinking cup-a-soup. Everyone I knew was away; I had been invited to Christmas at Adrien's grandmother's but of course now that wasn't happening. We'd broken up a fortnight before but I was too embarrassed to tell my family, so those festive weeks had passed in coldness and silence. On Boxing Day I dragged myself out for a walk – the day was dark and misty and shrouded me in perfect gloom. As I was passing the Père Lachaise on my way back home it started to feather with snow, which turned to slush, which turned to rain. It rained so hard I had run into the cemetery and taken shelter in the tomb of a family called Descombes, and as the rain grew heavier a whimper escaped me. It occurred to me that nobody could hear so I let the whimper build to a cry until I was howling so loud it felt like my throat would tear. It felt amazing to scream so loud. I screamed out all the sadness and silence I'd held in for a thousand years and when the rain eased I stopped and sat down with my head in my hands. Then I called my dad.

Come home, he'd said. Even for a few weeks. But I couldn't afford it and I didn't want to ask him for money, and also I didn't want to leave.

If I had gone home then, the accident wouldn't have happened. Or would it? Would I have found another way to hurt myself? Was it destined that on that day, January 18, I would die, or almost die, a gruesome death?

Bérénice Bayeaux buzzes me in. Her reception area is empty. One crumpled *Paris Match*. I wish my name was Bérénice Bayeaux, something that whispered in the breeze. Her reception area is as cold as I remember, but it was winter last time I was here. It feels like a morgue after the warm day outside. I miss Kate suddenly, who was here with me then, her warm hand on mine, same hand as mine, same hand as Mum's.

'*A-lors!*' says Bérénice Bayeaux, sweeping into the reception as an old man hobbles out of her room. I stand up and she turns me around gently. Her hands are icicles. 'You look a lot better than when I saw you last.'

'I'm feeling a *lot* better.'

'*Venez.*'

She ushers me into her room, which is also cold. It looks different to how I remember it. Way fewer colours, the walls still and sombre.

'Tell me about your recovery in Australia.'

I tell her about living with Dad, the stay in hospital after the reaction to the medications. The Chinese doctor and the chiropractor I saw who helped a lot.

'*Chiropracteur?*'

Chiropractic is seen as voodoo science in France. I had never been to a chiropractor before the accident either; the image I'd always had of them is the 'cracking of the neck'. But the Chinese doctor I was seeing recommended a colleague of hers. She trusted him completely, and I trusted her.

'He's the reason I have some flexibility in my neck now,' I tell Bérénice. 'I'm sure of it.'

She is not convinced. I tell her how the doctors in Australia had never seen a brace like mine before, how when I was in hospital they would gather around me, examining it and taking notes.

'Yes,' she says. 'It's new technology.' She points to my scarf. 'Take this off.'

I take it off and stand, feeling vulnerable.

She instructs me to turn this way, then that. I can move my neck a little way now, though my upper body is still stiff, robotic, and refuses to stop moving with my neck, as a protective measure. Each time my neck gets to a certain point I think of the man on the highway and panic. Also, it hurts.

'*Intéressant. Déshabillez-vous.*'

I stand naked from the top up and Bérénice looks me over. At first I was shy when she looked right at my tits and I laughed about it on the phone with Kiki later. 'She was checking me out!' But, of course, she was observing my body alignment, and anyway she was French – tits are no big deal here, they're out all summer long.

'Good, good,' she says and puts me in the chair with the chin strap. She rubs my naked back with oil and her cold, cold, hands, working her way up to my neck. Tears push up in me with the movement of her hands and slide down my face into the spongey prop beneath my chin.

'You are very stiff. You are in pain?'

I never know how to answer this. What is pain? This constant fluff, sore eyes, rigidity, the urge to cry each time I wake? The knowledge I had frightened others, a general sense of foreboding, rickety hands? 'No. Well, yes. I'm sleeping on my friend's floor on a hard mattress. And the plane over … My neck is sore and my head aches but I'm used to it.'

'Mmmm.' She keeps rubbing. 'You are getting better. The break in the bone is healed, but it is good that you wear the scarf, something to support your neck. You should be wearing a proper collar, but this is fine and of course less ugly. You need to sleep somewhere better.'

'I just have two more nights on the floor, then I'll have a bed.'

'Okay, then good. And you must come back to see me every week. I'll book you in for today in one week.'

'Oh no, I'll be in Portugal.'

She looks up, concerned.

'Just for a month. Then I'll be back.'

'Well, you will need to be *extremely* careful in Portugal. Rest the neck. If you have bad pain you should come back and see me – it is not too far. You will need many months of *rétablissement* – you know this? You have a prescription from Salpêtrière? Be serious, or you will have pain the rest of your life.'

Okay, okay, I think. I don't want to do this shit. I feel fine, I will be fine.

She hands me an ugly blue neck brace, like the one they put me in on the stairwell after the accident. An Aspen collar. I guess they call them that because of ski accidents. At first, when people asked what had happened to me – and they did this a surprising amount in the *quartier*, especially old ladies, hurrying across the street to ask *mais mademoiselle — qu'est ce qui vous êtes arrivé?* — I would tell them the actual story and watch them go into all manner of tailspins and rants, which would send me into one myself. Soon after, I started saying *accident de ski*, which was succinct, effective, and quite cosmopolitan.

'Wear this on the plane and any time your neck gets tired. The scarf is good, but this is designed specifically. You will need it from time to time.'

Out in the reception area I hand Bérénice my Carte Vitale. How I love my Carte Vitale, my plastic piece of French membership. Most of her fee is covered by it, but I don't know if it's still valid, now that I've left the country and come back. To my relief her machine doesn't reject it, and nobody comes to arrest me for fraud.

⁓

On my last night in Paris, Nadine begs me to come to a party with some of our old mutual friends from the theatre schools, which I couldn't bear, so I tell her I have the marionette show. Now I have to go, I realise; Nadine will know if I lie about it. I still can't bear the thought of going back to the 20ᵗʰ. The theatre is out near the Porte de Montreuil, so I won't need to go anywhere near Chine or Pelleport or the Hôpital Tenon, but still, it's the line 3 and I'll have to go past Gambetta. I tell myself to stop being so dramatic and when the 3 arrives I get on it and enjoy the same homely feeling I had when going in the other direction, remembering the deep feeling of independence of shopping for little things on my way up the rue des Pyrénées in the growing dark, a baguette, some noodles, a cheese perhaps if I had the money, a few vegetables for a soup, walking the streets back to my own place *à moi*, with nobody inside it but me, my things as I'd left them in the morning, my telephone with its *messagerie*, my stove top, the smell of fresh paint. The 20ᵗʰ was like a real, old Paris village and I felt part of the culture for the first time in my own way, not as a tourist or a girlfriend or a student. I paid *taxes* now, I had insurance, a kettle. If I could just get through the holidays, the sun would come out and my new life would begin.

The theatre is in a street I don't know, below a sweet old building and, once inside, I forget which part of the city I'm in. Every small red seat is taken and the mood is warm and my heart full for Paris on this, a Tuesday night in a small theatre, a marionette show for god's sake, sold out. Antoine, the director of the play, is up the back and looks blankly my way before recognising me and waving.

'Salut! T'es revenue!'

The lights go down. The piece is captivating, using the *marionnettes à gaine*, the old wooden puppets manipulated with hands up their skirts. Hand puppets, essentially, though that sounds far too banal for what they are – hand-carved faces and arms that, when moved with precision by such actors, come to life and evoke such emotion it's hard not to cry. Something in their innocence, their alien-ness I suppose, like that of the *bouffon* only more delicate, sensitive. Actors in black move their bodies without hiding themselves – but in service to the puppets we forget them, eyes glued to the characters, every hinge brought to life with mastered articulation. The actors' entire beings are engaged; they are acting. Their acting is what makes the puppets real. The marionette is a dead object until someone puts life into it. And yet, the marionette will never die.

The story is of an old man and woman living in an old house full of mice; the mice scurry around the sets and though I try, I can't make out their operators or what kind of marionettes they are – *marottes* – stick puppets, perhaps, or are they just pictures attached to hands or feet? I don't want to know, I'm swept up in the story. The old couple are poor but happy, though they keep having problems with their house and it leads to a fight; the house falls down and they're out in the cold and have to hold on to each other for warmth. A kind young woman, another *gaine*, takes them in and the old man falls in love with her and the old woman gets angry and leaves, but the young woman doesn't want the old man so he ends up back in the street. Eventually the old woman finds the old man and they rebuild their house and the mice come back and that's the end.

I forget for a moment where I am. I clap then slip out into the street before Antoine or any of the actors see me, but as I head down the street I hear Antoine call and turn back, apologising. My heart is racing, I'm not sure why. Sorry to be running off, I tell him, I loved the show but I'm running late to meet someone. He is kind, saying they missed me in the show and asking after my health. I tell him I'm great, fully recovered, then he is interrupted and I give him a wave and move away, back through the quiet streets towards the métro.

It's darker here over the hill, where the lights of central Paris don't reach. My mind plays with me, daring me to turn down the rue Belgrand and walk up the rue Pelleport, alongside the Hôpital Tenon where I lay bleeding as the madman in the next room screamed, to Sophie's apartment with its black iron and glass door, the guillotine awaiting inside, The Widow, The Silence-Maker, The Machine, The Regretful Climb, Louis XVI's necktie. My body dares me, in that same way it dares me to pull my pants down on stage and I have to fight to push it in the right direction, back toward the métro, almost running to the platform to jump in a carriage. I see blood. Hear screams. Am falling. Am nowhere. Two teenage girls sitting opposite me compare nail designs. I can't breathe. In for – how many? Sophie's stairwell, in my eyes. Is there a higher rail there now? Have they enclosed the lift shaft? Are there signs saying *ATTENTION DANGEREUX*, is it roped off with red and white stripes, is there a stain where my body lay?

I've missed my stop. Where am I? The train carriage is empty. Malesherbes. I get off and change platforms, far away from it now, the opposite end of the line. I watch the stations go by one by one as they lead me back to République, eyes wide in case I miss it and end up back up there, the haunted *quartier*. Force my brain to shut it off. Portugal tomorrow, a new city, the play, the girls from school, a moment to digest this moment in Paris before returning to start again. The thoughts won't switch off. The train too slow. The train that night while my head was stuck, coming for me, the sound of it approaching, deafening, the need to get out of its way. That moment of realisation: this is it. Black.

République. I get off the train. I can never set foot in the 20th again.

Back at Nadine's I can't sleep. The pain is bad, shooting up through my head and out of my eyes, out my shoulders, down my legs. I need to get out of Paris, now. I get up and sit by the window and watch the sun rise over the canal, the promise of another warm day. By the time Nadine wakes I've packed up and am ready to go.

'But you've got hours,' she says, rubbing her eyes.

'I like to be early. Can I leave this suitcase here?'

'Sure. Can I wear your stuff?'

'Course, my love.'

She pushes my things into a corner and grabs my smaller suitcase to help me down the stairs.

'You don't need to do that.'

'I want to.'

I thank her profusely for having me in her warm little den. 'Thank Didier for letting me squeeze him out.'

'He never comes here, he has a shiny apartment with a real bed.'

'How boring!'

'Yeah, in the 6th.'

'Woah.'

'You can always stay with me when you're back to do the show.'

'You're sweet, but I've got the Récollets.'

'Yeah, but if you'd rather.'

'We'll be just across the canal from each other.'

'And I'll keep my ears open for cheap apartments.'

'Thanks. Anything starting end of summer.'

'In the 10th?'

'Yeah, or the 19th, 11th. Just not the 20th.'

She hugs me on the bottom stair and I squeeze her and pull back, afraid to fall into her softness, eager to get out of the city in a way I've never felt.

'Courage with the show,' she says in the doorway. 'And don't forget, be Franco.'

A lady passing by trailing a shopping caddy turns to glare at us. We laugh and I walk up the canal, turning to wave as I move out of sight but Nadine is gone.

The train out to Orly isn't fast enough. How I miss hard drugs, the pain they take away. The ibuprofen and paracetamol take a slight edge off, as does Paris disappearing, for now.

My phone beeps: a message from M.

Bon voyage!

Six Letters

Portugal is a disaster. By the time M arrives at the end of the second week I am slumped in the dark at the back of the theatre watching my script be mutilated.

Things had started well. Tez and her mother met me at the airport. Tez looked tanned and fit – solid on her home turf. She had taken skin. Her mother, Marina, as petite and gentle as Tez was strong and brusque, wanted to take me the long way through the centre of Porto and across a famous bridge built by the Eiffel company, which drove Tez nuts.

'Sorry Jayne, *elle est <u>chiante!</u>*'

Marina was not a pain in the arse. We connected instantly; her warm, bright face turning to me in the backseat to wink – comrades in view appreciation. Marina spoke not a word of English and just a tiny bit of French, so was silent with me, combative in Portuguese in the front seat with Tez. Tez spoke okay English and outside of the theatre we spoke mostly that, but we always worked in French, as we had in school. French Élodie and Spanish Ana both spoke no English. Marie-France spoke a little English, in a sweet birdlike way, as if she was about to get in trouble. Faye still spoke French with an American drawl and Meg's was prim. I'd been told my accent was good, but I was still sometimes mistaken for a German.

The first week was a blast. It was like we'd been freed from the zoo, all in love with each other and excited to start our new life together. I pretended I was a Lecoq instructor and had them running and rolling around the stage, playing games, warming the space, which they didn't need me to lead, they just did it anyway. I had them doing vocal exercises – something we'd never done at Lecoq – to prepare to project in the vast auditorium, which reminded me more of the kind of theatre we'd do dance concerts in at home than the dusty black boxes we were used to. I could see that the girls thought the vocal exercises were dumb and just wanted to get straight into creation, but they followed me, I was *director*. We built scenes from the script and from the storyboard I'd made, which again they raised their eyebrows at, *mais bon*. We were adapting to a new way of working.

At night Marina would serve dinner, usually cod, and leave us alone to eat. We sat around a large dining table and discussed ideas, it was merry. The house was a hulking stone mansion, austere and vast, with a sloping terracotta roof. My bed was soft. Too soft, but I would never complain; it was far better than Nadine's floor-bed.

The week went by fast. We tried all kinds of things that brought the script to life and led to surprises and weirdnesses I couldn't have imagined. The idea was that the absurd humour, loudness and enormity of what's happening in the mind of Martha should contrast with the quiet physicality of how she appears to the real world. We should be shocked as the audience at the bizarre shit that is actually going on in there, and feel terrified, titillated, on a knife's edge. This lovely, dish-washing lady, mother, well-dressed, put-together, is actually a horror show only multiple women could represent. The scenes naturally began to fall into place. Tez suggested a fight scene between herself and Marie-France – Martha fighting with her inner world. I thought it was a great idea and made a further suggestion, modifying it a little. There was a slight note to Tez's capitulation. Just a note. I wondered if I was over-reacting.

It was the second week that things started going downhill. We'd spent the weekend making posters for *Marta Vai ao Mercado* and plastering them around town. The box office opened and tickets began to sell; the local press started calling, administrative questions arose regarding the program, the seating, interviews, signage out the front of the theatre, ticket sellers. Because it was Tez's home town, she was on the front-line. On the Monday there was a slight edge to her mood, which affected Meg. It didn't matter, we were still moving forward, rehearsing the scenes that were working, pulling apart the clunky ones and putting them back together in new ways. But by Tuesday there was a definite scratchy feeling in the air that by Wednesday had infected the whole group. I called an early lunch break to try to lighten things.

'It's coming together,' I told them at Fernando's, the café down the road from the theatre. 'We just need to push through these next few days to break the back of it.'

Marie-France nodded and sipped her coffee, saying she could feel the strength of the story now. We were sharing a room and she had been giving me intel each night. She reported unrest, but nothing I couldn't sense already.

Faye was positive, said she loved the opening scene and she had a sore stomach from laughing so hard in the fight scene. Élodie remarked that a few of the scenes were even better than the ones in the school version.

Meg and Tez ate their sandwiches.

That afternoon I asked Tez to start her trajectory from upstage right and she put her hands on her hips. '*Pourquoi?*'

'No reason,' I said, 'it just balances the *plateau* better.'

'But why would I come from there?'

'Are you asking a *character* question?' I asked her. An insult. She wasn't playing a *person*, she was playing a *dynamic*.

'No,' she said, 'I just don't see why I'd go from upstage to downstage in that moment.'

Umm, just do it, I wanted to say. *Franco*. 'Trust me Tez, I can see from out here.'

'Okay okay,' she said, slumping her way across the stage.

I think that was the moment it died. Her body, slumping. I don't think in the whole time at Lecoq I saw a single hair on someone's arm slump.

You don't *slump*. There is no *slumping in theatre*. Would you *slump* with Ariane Mnouchkine? I wanted to ask. With Peter Brook? Would you *slump* with Jacques Lecoq?

I am not Jacques Lecoq. But, I felt, we were carrying his spirit of creation. It was hard, but we were headed somewhere unique, there were already sparks of it in the show.

But the slump had entered the room. Meg's mind was slumped even if her body didn't dare. Élodie began questioning my propositions. Faye got frustrated. Marie-France's lovely brow furrowed. Awkward silences rang through the space and an anxious air stank things up as we realised that we might not be ready before M arrived for tech week. I saw panic in Tez's eyes. Was it worse for her because her friends and family would be coming to the show? Was she tired of having us all in her house? Was it me? Was I a hopeless director? Was it because I was weakened, constantly grabbing at my scarf, pulling it tighter, unable to wield the same power I had at school, when I could run and jump and flip on demand, be part of the team, muscle it out with everyone from within the scrum?

That night, Marie-France and I stayed up picking the piece apart, trying to find ways to get it back. We planned scenes, typed out notes, set the entire play out in a storyboard. The girls watched the presentation the next morning and listened. The day passed productively. Then on Thursday, a devastating shift. Tez began giving direction herself, instructing the others on stage without consulting me. Meg followed suit, then Élodie; Faye and Marie-France, with a few pleading looks out towards me, fell into line – what could they do? – and before I knew it they were basically working without me. I watched from the stalls, dumbfounded. The machine that had been our way of working over the past two years had taken over. They trusted it more than they trusted me.

I told them I was going for a walk. My head hurt, my neck throbbed, there was a sharp pain in the tendons that linked my eyes to my brain. Worse, my heart was sore. My script was going from what I had hoped to be a structured and powerful account of a woman's meltdown to a series of banal vignettes. The group clearly didn't want me as director, didn't need me. Oh Jacques, what should I do?

I went back to the house and sat with Marina on the patio. She and I had hit it off from the start. I would speak in French in case she could pick up some of it, but even if she did, she responded in Portuguese, which might as well have been a rubber band pinging. The only things I could say now were *Tudo bem?* – how are you? – and *muito obrigada* – thanks very much. But we'd found a language of non-comprehension in which to communicate, and I felt that, in some place in ourselves, we did understand each other. Now I sat telling her I was scared about the play and wasn't sure what to do about it, and I wasn't sure about M coming over. I told her I still missed Adrien even though I hated him, I missed my dad, I was worried about my neck and whether I'd ever recover enough to be able to do the things I used to. I was scared at the idea that I'd been changed forever, scared of being scared. Marina answered me calmly, as though we were having the most natural conversation in the world, and I took the feeling of her words. At one point she repeated something a few times, which I was dying to decipher but couldn't for the life of me. She wanted me to understand too, but she just kept saying it louder. I told myself she was saying, it's okay, you're doing great. I smiled at her and said *muito obrigada.* She gave me a strange smile, like that was a weird thing to say.

The dinner table that night was funereal. Conversation perfunctory. Faye slipped me looks, Marie-France looked glum, Ana was awkward, Meg stoic and Tez as cold as cold. We'd been in the trenches together – we knew how to get through this. Didn't we?

⌒

On Friday afternoon, the theatre door opens, letting in a burst of daylight.

M.

He stands blind at the top of the stairs, relaxed energy cutting through the space like a prison visitor. His sandy hair is messy, clothes crumpled.

Marina is behind him, she must have brought him straight from the airport. She shuts the door to the outside world, leaving him standing there, eyes adjusting.

I shimmy through the seats and up to him. 'Hi there!'

'Hi.'

I lead him down to the stage to introduce him to the girls, who stop their scene. They're all warm and excitable; Faye hugs him, Tez shakes his hand, Ana and the French girls kiss him on both cheeks.

'How are things progressing?' he asks.

Shy looks all round. A mix of non-comprehension of his laconic Australian accent and awkwardness over the show. The girls speak and I translate where needed, good good, getting closer, etc. etc.

'Thank you for being come here,' says Tez.

They get back to it and I lead him to a spot towards the middle of the theatre. They're rehearsing the cacophony scene, the climax of the show. I have a thousand things to ask and tell M but we sit in silence and watch.

'It needs to start more quietly,' I mutter to myself. Then I remember M is watching and that I'm still director. Shame and determination propel me forward in my seat.

'It needs to start quieter!' I call out when they stop. 'There needs to be a longer build up to when Marie-France screams. It needs to start imperceptibly and end in apocalypse.'

Tez turns around but is unable to see me in the dark. I get up and move past M towards the stage, but she has turned back to the group. I can't hear what they're saying and by the time I've reached the stage they've reassembled and are about to start the scene again.

'Tez? Did you hear what I said?'

'Yeah, that's what we're doing.'

But when they start again it's not what they're doing at all. The scene is losing the action, becoming *played*. It's not *juste*.

'Interesting dynamic …' says M as I sit back down beside him.

I've sent him a few messages explaining things so he's not surprised, but he tells me he hadn't expected it to be this bad. 'They're not even listening to you.'

They move on to another scene, and it's all wrong wrong wrong. The entire crux of the play is emptying through a sinkhole. 'Nooo,' I moan into my hands. I can't bear it. I can see Marie-France is about to cry. Oh, please, just kill me.

M whispers, 'Wanna go for a walk?'

Outside the theatre is another world. He looks glorious. Sanity personified, plane-fermented, in his scruffy t-shirt and jeans. We hug. He's never felt my body so close. We step back, it's weird. The last time he saw me I was out of the Cage but still extremely fragile. We hadn't even hugged when I left.

'You look so different …'

I laugh. 'Will you still like me Cageless?'

'I did have a soft spot for it.'

I lead him towards Fernando's, and as Fernando brings us thick black coffee and a *pastéis de nata* M tells me about the plane trip, the tenants he found for his apartment, the thrill of leaving his job and life behind. He describes his band's final gig, how he strummed the last note of the last song, put his guitar in its case and got in a cab straight to the airport. 'It's liberating,' he says, 'to leave it all behind and be here with just my guitar and a suitcase. Life feels light.'

'I wish this theatre situation was light,' I say. 'You've landed in some heavy shit. A thousand tonnes of Tez.'

He wants all the details so I start from the beginning, reassuring him that it will all work out, at school it was often a mess until the last minute.

'They overthrew my dictatorship!' I laugh, telling him about Nadine's advice.

'But this is a full-length show. You have to have a leader.'

'I agree. I had hoped that was me. Who leads your band?'

'Me.'

'I can see that. You seem like a natural leader. I've never been good at it. But I know this play needs it. I know – you direct it!'

'The last show I did the music for, the director was a fortress. Nobody dared mess with that.'

'It's just not the way we're used to working. We're all creators, we're used to fighting it out together to make a play.'

'But how do you maintain an hour-long show like that?'

'I know. I see the way we worked at school as a tool for generating ideas and short pieces, which we then go on and turn into form with a script and director.'

'That makes sense.'

'I don't think the girls see it that way. I guess I thought we could have it both ways.'

'The road to Clusterfuck.'

We go back to the auditorium where they are winding down for a break. Tez shows M the control room for the lighting and sound and he spends the rest of the afternoon climbing ladders and testing speakers. We want simple lighting effects to show the contrast in states between her inner world and the supermarket. There will be no music except for the opening and closing of the piece, and we've all agreed on two pieces M has adapted from another play he worked on, the first a strange electro piece and the second a guitar and keyboard piece with a big swell in the middle. We want it Lecoq simple. If the show is great, we were taught, you shouldn't need the bells and whistles.

We all drink a beer at the bar across the street and walk home together. Back at the house, Tez shows M around. She had asked when I arrived, with a cheeky look, if I wanted him to stay in my room, but I said no. That would have been weird. He will sleep in her brother's room. Tez's father and two brothers have fled the house on a long camping trip, so he's the only boy. I'm sharing with Marie-France but the others mostly have their own rooms – the house is enormous.

At dinner that night the girls fawn over M like they've never seen a man before, tripping over their varying levels of English. Marina stays to eat with us this time, another meal of ghastly cod. Tez translates her questions and M's answers, though I'm not sure Tez is understanding M herself, with his expressions and drawl. She soon gives up, she can't keep up with M and Marina doesn't care anyway, happier to smile and listen.

Maybe M is what we needed to pry open our closed dynamic. His presence softens things in rehearsals for the first few days, but the girls continue to freeze me out, just in a slightly more sociable way. M is respectful of them all and his suggestions are subtle and sensitive. The house technical manager, Marco, comes to work with M on sound and lights. For a few days the cloud seems lifted, but then, midway through the third week, during another rehearsal of my favourite part of the script, Tez stops midway and says, '*C'est pas juste!*'

My hackles rise. How *dare* she? To claim knowledge of what is and is not *juste* was always the domain of the *profs* at school – masters of a craft honed over decades. I glare at her. Her declaration is the greatest insult; it says that neither my words nor my direction contain any truth of real life, the meat of existence, the marrow of being. Perhaps the play is not *juste* yet, but it is on its way to something, and Tez has just rammed her heavy foot on its backbone.

I rise. '*Bon*, I'll leave you to explore what's *juste* then Tez, wouldn't want to muddy your knowledge of *justesse*.'

M follows me out of the theatre. The light hurts my eyes. We walk in silence to Fernando's. M orders lunch as I sit with my face in my hands.

'The people have spoken,' I say through my fingers as he sits opposite me.

'I have a suggestion,' he says, pausing.

'Yes?' I say, trying to hurry him up.

'Let's forget about it all for a sec.'

This is revolutionary to me. My nose has been pressed so tight to the show I've forgotten there was any more to life. Tomorrow is M's birthday, he tells me. He suggests we plan something fun – dinner or a lunch or something. Without the girls.

'Imagine having a day off,' I say, looking out the window.

'Now you're talking.'

I didn't mean it seriously, the idea fills me with theatre terror. Then it occurs to me it could give us all some much-needed space. If the girls have a day without me lurking around, perhaps they'll leap ahead and feel more secure about the show. M has done all his setting-up now, he's not needed. Marco can operate.

As we finish our food, the idea settles. When the girls enter the café for lunch and I suggest it to them, they're surprised at first, then agree. Their faces are wan. We ask Tez where we could go for a day trip and she recommends Espinho, a beautiful beach town about an hour's drive away.

The next morning M and I rise early and borrow Marina's car. The winding route to Espinho is liberating and we talk all the way there, him filling me in on Dad, who he kept visiting when I was away, my sister and brothers who he met too, and his own family. I tell him about Paris and how I'd been happy to be back, but glad to leave. He said that sounded normal, given the circumstances. That made me feel better, I was worried I never wanted to return there while knowing that I do. M has a way of making things that are heavy or contradictory feel light and normal.

We arrive in Espinho at lunchtime. The beach is nice, but I should have remembered we're Australian. The sand is grey and the water murky, but the great thing about European beaches is you don't have to pack a lunch, you can sit at a restaurant with your feet in the sand. The sun is hot on the tops of our heads and I can see M's forehead turning red as we eat green oysters and drink beer in an ugly little bar. God it feels good to be away from the girls. God it feels good to be hanging out with M. I realise we've never had fun before in the outside world. We dissect the show and the group and after another beer I order champagne and they bring us some good cheap *cava*.

'*Feliz aniversário!*'

'You speak Portuguese!'

'I looked it up and wrote it on my hand!'

'Of course you did!'

We drink two glasses each then M remembers he has to drive later so we jump in the sea to sober ourselves up and the water is so cold it takes our breath away.

'Have you been to Lisbon?' I ask him as we sit drying on the sand.

'No, have you?'

'No, but I want to. In my head it's paradise.'

'Mine too.'

'I've been dreaming of fleeing there.'

'Yeah, this is theatre hell.'

'Hell on many levels.'

'Perhaps you should leave?'

'Ha.'

You can't leave theatre. To even consider it is a cardinal sin. You go down with the ship. M laughs when I tell him this, my face deathly serious.

'Have you ever left a band?' I ask.

'Yes, I just did.'

'Oh yeah, I forgot. How did it feel?'

'Terrible. The drummer cried on stage. Tears all over the drum kit.'

That's so sad, I tell him, and he says, 'Yeah, but it's been over for a long time. You have to know when to call it.'

'Are you sure you made the right call?'

'Definitely.'

'It wasn't premature?'

'It was the opposite of premature.'

'So you escaped and came to a new prison. Theatre prison.'

'Ha. It's fine for me, great actually. It gave me the push I needed to leave Australia. Tough for you though. I say you give it one last go and if it's shit we flee.'

'You'd come?'

'For sure.'

'To Lisbon?'

'Anywhere. Our code can be *six letters starting with L*. Also, I'm not sure how much more cod I can eat.'

'You can't complain, you've just arrived.'

The sky clouds over. We walk back up the beach towards a little café we passed in the town on our way down to the beach, a place full of old men and races on the TV. We order coffees at a plastic table. I pull my hair back, frizzy from the sea.

'You're not wearing your scarf,' says M.

I clutch my neck. Reach for my bag, check that it's there. The bag is soft with the wool, thank god.

'The saltwater did it good,' I say, balling the wool in my fist.

'Put it back on if it makes you feel comfortable.'

'No, I might see how it feels to keep it free for a bit.'

A pang of emotion wells in me and I fight the urge to cloak it, allowing myself to sit and look at M and let him see the skin of my neck. We smile at each other, sitting in silence, then he stands to pay the bill and we walk out into the street. Dark clouds have almost completely congested the sky, and the sea at the bottom of the hill has turned a deep muddy green. A few determined rays poke through the clouds to create an almost-surreal display of purple and orange.

'I think we should kiss,' says M beside me.

'I agree,' I say, turning my body to face him.

He reaches towards me and kisses my lips. It's sweet, like teenagers.

'That felt good,' I say. 'More?'

He moves towards me again, my neck rod-still, and it's longer this time but just as sweet.

We laugh a bit, shy, and don't do it again, choosing to keep it like that, in its little box. It doesn't have to mean anything. As we walk to the car I wind my scarf back around my neck, a curious fashion plate I'm sure, with my bikini top and shorts.

'I wonder how much a flight to Lisbon costs from here?' he says as we approach the car.

'Wonder if we could drive there right now?'

M almost drives into a ditch on the way out of Espinho, misjudging his position on the road due to driving on the unfamiliar side, and my body seizes up but then we laugh and laugh as we hurtle through the fields, my feet out the window and the wind in my hair, Latino music loud on the stereo. As we drive around a hill face I scream out the window: 'PORTUGAL!! *JE T'AIME! JE T'AIIIIIME*' like Betty Blue in the movie, and it feels so good and freeing to be in a car that we decide to waste all Marina's petrol exploring the countryside and the suburban towns, watching people in squares, outside bars, kids playing summer games in the street. It's late by the time we get back to the house, and we creep upstairs and stand for a moment in the dark. He reaches for my hand and gives me another light kiss before whispering goodnight and splitting off to his room.

Six letters starting with L. The next day I whisper the words to M in the stalls and later he says them to me during a discussion with Tez. At the end of that day, I say it as we clear the dishes and the next day it's spoken over six times throughout the morning. At lunch M suggests we walk. Under a tree he says, 'We need to leave.'

'But I've told you I can't, it's a cardinal sin.'

'You haven't been here for a while now. They've already kicked you off.'

He's right. They've made the decision. Still, the idea is sickening, like leaving my baby on the roadside.

'Look,' M says, 'without wanting to be your big brother, you're under stress. I can see you're in pain, your scarf is so tight it's going to choke you. But also, this is *bullshit*. I've seen a lot of fucked shit in theatre and music but nothing as bad as this.'

'Where would we go? Lisbon?'

'No. Paris. Where you have support. We're going there anyway. We can be there in a matter of hours.'

'But we've got nowhere to stay. My room at the Récollets doesn't come up for weeks.'

'My friend's room is available any time.'

'I suppose I can stay at Nadine's.'

He sees my defeated look.

'We'll work something out,' he says. 'Let's just get out of here.'

The thought of leaving suddenly fills me with light.

'Think it over tonight,' says M. 'We can make a call in the morning.'

I sleep badly, neck crunched in the soft pillow. But the decision was made in my body with him under the tree. The next morning, buttering toast, I call to him across the breakfast table.

'Five letters, starting with P.'

The girls think we're talking crosswords.

He has already tentatively booked a flight for lunchtime. At the breakfast table I attempt to deliver the news without emotion. It is received for the cardinal sin that it is.

ÉLODIE:
C'est pas POSSIBLE!

JAYNE:
I can't be here. It's bad enough watching my script be tossed, but you don't need me, I'm hampering you. You know what you want to do. So do it.

They can't believe it. Tez's face is stormy but resolute. Marie-France is in tears. Faye's head is in her hands, *fuck fuck fuck fuck fuck*. Marina smiles as she sits down with her eggs.

JAYNE:
I'll be there in Paris to see the show. You can call me if you want help. But it's better for all of us if I'm not physically here.

TEZ:
What about M?

M:
I'm going too. The lights and music are all set up – I've shown Marco, Tez, he knows what to do. I'll also be in Paris, to set things up there and make any changes you want then.

I can see each of them have different things to say, but are holding tight to the last threads of the group, the fact that they must go forward.

They leave the room, a funeral procession, saying goodbye one by one, a range of emotions. I keep it together, encouraging them. It will all be fine, it's good, it's fine, it'll be great, better this way. I leave a note for Marie-France apologising, though I know she gets it, when I told her last night she agreed I should go. Marina waits with us for the taxi downstairs as we attempt to thank her profusely for her hospitality. When the cab arrives, she grabs my arm and says in strangled French:

Un … n'est rien.

She gives me the same warm smile from the patio. I'm not sure what to say, so I say *si. Ciao!* We climb into the cab. 'One is nothing?' Did she mean '*On n'est rien*', as in one – a person – is nothing? Does she mean one person alone is nothing – as in, we should partner up? Is she encouraging me to be with M? Was she saying *de rien*, as in 'no problem' for having us? Did she mean it's all meaningless? Was that what she was trying to say to me on the patio that day? Was she meaning it in a positive way? I want to go back, but we're already on the highway. M squeezes my hand. I give it no more thought. We are hurtling towards something new.

Hotel Love

Arriving in Paris with M is to see it with new eyes. He has been here before, he told me on the train, but that was 12 years ago, when he was 22 playing the international tennis circuit. I didn't know you were a tennis player, I told him. Lots of things you don't know about me, he said, and smiled, looking out the window. A clichéd thing to say, and he knew it, but it was also true. I had no idea who he was in the world; what kind of restaurants he liked, was he sociable, would he be fun to be with in Paris or a drag, would he need me, would he be a different person? So far, he was delightful. His excitement was exciting; he wanted pastries straight off the plane, and he was bristling in the stinking train as we rushed through the suburbs. It was overcast for July, the houses and fields grey. I thought about asking him if he'd heard of the syndrome tourists are hospitalised for, so shocked by the reality of Paris in contrast to their dreams that they have psychological breaks, but I didn't. It was fun just watching him watch. His long thumb caressed the handle of his suitcase as he stared out at the suburbs shooting past. The thumb was steady, insistent. I was very much liking the thumb.

'Dad would say you have hands like a man who has never lifted a brick in his life,' I said at one point, tired of the silence.

M smiled. 'He has said that.' And turned his head back to the view.

At the airport I booked us a room at the Hôtel Amour. They'd just had a cancellation. It was my last choice – expensive, hip, with a very leading name – but the cheap hotels I knew were booked out, and we both agreed tonight we should stay together, celebrate that we got out, that we were in Paris. We deserved it after what we'd been through, and also, it was pretty clear to both of us what was going on. One night in the Hotel Love. I thought of my neck and the warning about movement and wondered if you could die by sex, *petite mort*. You can't stay in the Hôtel Amour and not have sex. The Hôtel Amour *is* sex. When my friends Gabriella and Marcus stayed there to celebrate their engagement, the walls were so lurid she said she couldn't sleep for the penises coming to get her.

We arrive at the Gare du Nord in the mid-afternoon. The sun has come out, bathing the vast, glass entranceway, and us, in vibrant gold.

'PAR-EEE!' I sing as we step through the doors, opening my arms and letting my luggage fall before quickly picking it back up again.

'*Je t'aaaime!!*' calls M to Paris in a gentle way, as excited as a calm man gets. We walk across the road to the Paris Nord Café, where we order a *demi* and a *sancerre* and some *chips paysannes* and sit in the window looking across the cobblestones back at the station, the people from everywhere, going everywhere.

'*Nous voilà!*' I say, and we clink glasses and the tepid wine tastes amazing.

'*Oui!*' he says.

'How's your French?'

'*Bon.*'

'Have you ever lived in a foreign city?'

'Only briefly, for tennis. Many cities, not very long.'

'Do you know to watch your shit?'

'Of course,' he says, moving his bag on to his lap.

'I've had everything stolen, many times.'

'I've had nothing stolen.'

We drink and smile. We did it. We're here.

'Let's make a pact to enjoy this day and forget about Portugal and not think about tomorrow and New York and where we're going to stay 'n shit.'

'Done.'

'Don't know why I'm talking like a gangster all of a sudden.'

'Neither do I.'

'Just making sure I'm looking out for you. It's a big city.'

'I'm a big boy.'

He looks around. 'Do you know this part of the city well?'

'Yep. The Récollets is just down that way, five minutes' walk. I'd only come here if I was going somewhere though, or meeting someone off the train. Or when all the bars in Paris are shut, these are open all night. And you?'

'*Pas du tout.* I was on the left bank mostly, the tourist bits.'

'Do you like Paris better or New York?'

'Not sure. I know New York better.'

'So, New York then?'

'Nah … not sure.'

'But if you had to pick.'

'I couldn't pick.'

'But if I held a gun to your head.'

'Then you'd have to shoot me.'

'I will shoot you now for not playing my game.'

He smiles. 'I thought we weren't thinking about tomorrow.'

'We're not.'

'Anyway, just so you know I have no intention of flying straight to New York. I'm going to stay until the play's over.'

'I don't care. I'm not thinking about tomorrow.'

He laughs. 'Shall we go to the hotel?'

I pay and guide him toward Magenta, across the chaotic boulevard, breathing in the homely smells of curry and exhaust, the sounds of traffic and people speaking French on their phones. I love this part of the North, I tell M. The rue Lafayette leading down to the 9th and the river, the boulevard heading up to Montmartre, the Bouffes du Nord Theatre and the crumbling old Louxor cinema, and down to my old neighbourhood in the 10th to République. Pure concrete and ancient grime. My hair fills with the soot of time and the sound of *life*. I take him the rue de Dunkerque way, then down the pretty rue Condorcet to the rue des Martyrs, where I stop outside a *primeur* and buy a punnet of *gariguettes*, my favourite strawberries. The man gives us a handful to try and M's face lights up in the sunshine. We suck on strawberries as we approach the Hôtel Amour, my neck dripping with sweat beneath the scarf, our suitcase wheels clunking on the pavement.

The hotel is unassuming, in a simple neighbourhood street. An understated supermodel greets us at reception like we're part of the in-crowd. We look so dishevelled I guess we could be rock stars, and there's M's guitar case. He seems neither nervous nor uncomfortable, unthreatened at being in an unfamiliar place speaking an unfamiliar language. The supermodel is looking at him in a certain way, and come to think of it, several women's eyes were on him like that as we walked here. I don't remember Adrien being looked at like that, though he had the Latin looks that in Australia would stop traffic. Here, sandy-haired M with his blue eyes and untamed vibe must be exotic to the Parisiennes.

We follow the supermodel to our room, past the fashion crowd drinking in the airy downstairs bar and up the stairs through a black lacquered corridor to a room at the end. 'The owner's favourite,' says the supermodel, opening the door. *'N'hésitez-pas si vous avez besoin de quoi que ce soit.'* She gives M a lingering look as though I'm not there and pulls the door shut. I wonder how many sex parties he's had, being a band guy – those chicks in the back rooms in hitched-up miniskirts – but he assures me, none, that only happens in movies.

The room is all black, like the corridor. Black velvet carpet, black walls, black bookshelves displaying 70s magazines with nubile young girls on them eyeing on us, *who, me?* The bed is white, too cool for legs, the mattress nestled on the soft carpet between two black lamps. There's something grown-up about being here, and deeply horny. We let our luggage fall and sink onto the soft bed. The ceiling is made of disco balls.

'Last night I was in Tez's brother's room looking at a poster of a gorilla,' M says.

'Thank god for you,' I say. 'I would have stayed until they devoured my corpse.'

I should be moving now, rolling over to touch him, performing lateral movements, small ones even, turning my head, swaying my hips like the girls in the magazines. I want to but my body is rigid, like I'm still in the brace. And I'm terrified. And embarrassed. Completely vulnerable. Being able to perform, do the act, stops you being *seen*.

'I just want you to know, I can't really … move.'

'You don't need to.'

He could have said, that's cool, backed away, felt dejected, got out a deck of playing cards. But he has no intention of this. That he would want to do it to me, despite my brokenness and the threat still present in my neck, is both disarming and deeply appealing. He is not afraid. I'm sure he knows it's unlikely I'll die, but there's still a chance a big movement could displace the bone.

When I was in the Cage, I'd fantasise about a no-faced man pulling my clothes purposefully aside beneath the construction to reveal my flesh, loosening my chin strap, undoing the velcro strap across my forehead, having his way with me as I lay unmoving. Now I feel a sort of phantom brace around me, and the fantasy is actually happening, only with a face and without the porny domination thing. M's face is soft, and there's that familiar stillness, the feeling that he knows what he is doing in this life and is not just putting it on. He touches my forehead where the velcro strap used to sit, tracing the lines where the moulded plastic once was, down the side of my face to my neck, the metal plates and knobs, the bars around my ribs. I take his hand and place it on my chest, in a part where there never was scaffolding. My body feels new, I'm discovering it with him. He traces my ribs, my right arm, my cheek. I close my eyes and let him trace the scars, my face still not quite mine. I blink my eyes open and tug at his t-shirt. He shimmies mine off, then everything except the scarf. I think of leaving it on as a protection against dying but wind it off to see how it will feel. Now I'm really naked. I put my hands on my neck, feel the soft, damp skin beneath. 'Do you want to put it back on?' he asks. I say no and he kisses my neck gently, moving his way down my body. It's not like I do nothing, I do the opposite of nothing, though I'm not moving. He does the moving.

He moves very well. Imagining the Cage around me eases the fear. Death is present, right there with me, but I have it under my control, I think. My body starts to shudder, a pleasurable shivering I've not experienced before. He likes it and stays with me, I'm losing my sense of control, I can feel it, the shuddering intensifies, I'm afraid, but it feels too good to stop. And I do die, but only in the French sense. Big death. He rolls off me gently and lies on his back catching his breath, before turning back towards me.

'Are you okay?'

'Yes.'

We lie in silence, looking at the disco balls. Eventually he gets up to open the curtains and lies back down with me naked in the early evening sun. I like that he doesn't care if anyone sees in, like a true Parisian. Sunlight invades me. Questions threaten to flood my mind and I can sense his too, but I push mine away and focus on our pact: no future. Just this moment. Just this night. He goes to the shower and I lie spreadeagled, wanting everything about this room to get inside me, the nudie girls, his scent, the sunshine, this feeling of abundance.

The fan clicks. The world feels far away.

The shower spurts and runs. I sit on the luscious carpet and start pulling on clothes. My knickers and jeans, his t-shirt from the floor that reads ERIC'S TOOLS. He comes into the room, hair hanging wet over his face, a ray of sunlight splitting him in two. He likes me in his t-shirt. It's a girlfriend thing to do, but whatever.

'Hungry?'

Burgers in the courtyard with the trendy people of Paris. I try and act cool, M just is. He doesn't seem to care what anyone thinks of him, including me – he doesn't need me to like him. I need everyone to like me, all the time, even this waiter now; I give him all my energy, hoping he will like me. I wonder if M would like Nadine. People who don't need to be liked don't always like each other. M likes me, I can feel that, as he knocks his knee gently with mine beneath the table. Why he would like me is a mystery, especially in the state I was in when we met. The state I'm still in.

After dinner there is more sex. More shudders. The night is warm and we leave the windows open, but the noise from the courtyard never dies down so M gets up around 3 am and closes them. When we wake it's raining. I have an idea. What if I ask to come early to the Récollets? I have sponsorship to stay there because of the play. You have to have a specific project, artistic, scientific or academic, and a month was already generous for the play's rehearsals and run. But it's worth asking. One thing I've learnt here is it's always worth asking.

I go to the window and call Chantal, as M sleeps. She sounds happy to hear from me, in her subdued way. The studio she booked for me isn't available until later in the month as planned, but she happens to have room 207 free, two doors down from my old room. It's unoccupied all summer. I do a little dance.

'Chantal, one more thing,' I say, after thanking her profusely. 'I'm here with a friend who has a project in Paris too. Would it be okay if I brought him?'

'What is his project?'

'He is a musician. He's making an album.'

'Okay, ça marche. We'll see you after 2 pm today.'

I hang up, a sense of lightness in my body. M turns towards me.

'Who was that? I love hearing you speak French.'

'I have a proposition,' I tell him, taking a pause. 'If we want it, we have a room in the Récollets.' I lie back down, pleased with myself. 'Starting today.'

M gives me a quizzical look.

'You don't have to come,' I say. 'You just always ask for more than you want and work back from there.'

'You want me to come with you to the Récollets?'

'Of course, I always planned to show it to you. Let's go over there. If you want to, you can stay tonight, and we can see about tomorrow tomorrow.'

He rolls onto his back. He likes the plan.

Room 207

Room 207 is the exact same layout as the room I lived in for two years while I was studying at Lecoq, but facing the opposite direction. I love that Chantal called room 205 *la tienne* on the phone because that's how I think of it, as still mine, with my posters on the walls, Kiki's bottle of vodka on the window ledge with Adrien's stinky cheeses and my optimistic geraniums. Someone else would have moved in there when I left last September, a scientist or researcher or an artist. Perhaps a performance group, like the four girls from Sydney who did a drag show for Nuit Blanche that Adrien laughed at in a way that irritated me and led us to a fight so big it became a public spectacle.

In the room between this room and 205 lived an American novelist and playwright who had been working on something at the Théâtre de la Ville. He lived with his teenaged son and used to smoke *gitanes* like Gainsbourg at the window in the hall looking out over the Gare de l'Est, which was an excellent place to stand but the smoke would come under my door and right up to my bed and I would wake feeling like I'd smoked ten packs. I smoked too but his cigarettes had a fervent, ugly smell. As I'm recalling this a draught of his tobacco wafts in beneath the door. I'm glad. I want to talk to him. I was too shy before, his age and experience intimidated me, though he was gentle and self-effacing.

When Chantal showed us in, I asked who else was living on the second floor now but she was too busy smiling at M. You always knew if Chantal liked you or not. She didn't love me, she tolerated me; I was always pestering her for something, the keys to the *cave* for rehearsals or a party, an extension on my rent, to sign some form or another. She never liked Adrien, not one bit, and I would feel the need to hide him.

The room has a dizzying effect on me. The bones are the same but in reverse, and the smaller details such as the wall cracks and knots in the wood beams are different, the tall concrete pylons painted red instead of green. It's the dream of being at home but everything's different. The sensation of having stepped through the looking glass. The mezzanine bedroom is the same as the one in 205 but with the bed in the opposite direction, which almost helps me forget Adrien as M and I have unmoving sex again. I was always so worried about being a corpse in bed, but I don't care right now. I won't be a corpse forever. Or maybe I will, I really like it. M doesn't seem to mind. Afterwards we shower, throw clothes on and go outside. He's hungry so I take him down the canal to the rue de Lancry to buy Lebanese sandwiches filled with nothing but sauces and tabouleh, which sounds insane but it's a Nadine specialty and delicious. He laps it up, dripping baba ganoush in a puddle alongside mine, and here he is, in the picture I couldn't imagine him in last month. A beer at Chez Prune, where the guys at the bar say hi and ask if I'm okay; they know the story because of Nadine and their concerned questions feel kind and family-ish. M can't understand a word they're saying but gets the gist and smiles and nods away. Nadine is nowhere in sight, which is good: she'd be annoyed to bump into me before I've told her I'm back, especially with a new 'friend'. I send her a message saying *Portugal a bust, you were right, back in Paris, call you tomorrow.*

I want to show M everything, right now, there's no tomorrow. We leave Chez Prune and stop for a stand-up beer in a shabby bar on the rue Lucien-Sampaix where old men watch the horse racing on the TV amongst piles of butts and discarded tickets. M loves this bar, and when we leave we decide that we'll stop to look at and taste anything that catches his interest as we walk. An *escargot*. A music school. The Marché

Saint-Martin. Fruit stalls – don't touch! Cheese … Outside the town hall with its impressive turrets and balconies a wedding crowd is gathered on the steps. I explain how the French usually have two ceremonies, a civil service and then a church service with a reception afterwards. As we move through the well-dressed crowd, M unwittingly positioning himself to protect me.

I ask if he's been married and he laughs and says no, not even close. He doesn't think he's the marrying type. He asks what Adrien and I had planned for our wedding.

'Do you honestly want to know?'

'I wouldn't have asked if I didn't.'

I tell him the full fantasy, though it's embarrassing to say it out loud. Afternoon lunch at his mother's country house in springtime, the grass all high, me in bare feet, Adrien too, an old wooden table there in the grass piled high with food with an old white lace tablecloth on it, stained with red wine. I saw it wild and festive, like in a Kusturica film, but without the chickens. Dresses torn, dancing into the night.

In fact, we hadn't actually done much real planning. I didn't even have an engagement ring. He had showed me some styles but I didn't like any of them and we'd fought so I'd looked for my own, it was more *pratique* anyway, and just to get an idea, I'd gone to the Place Vendôme and tried one on in the shape of a flower in Dior that I liked, and told Adrien and we tried to find a cheap version but never did.

M likes hearing stories about Adrien. He is intrigued by him. I ask about the girlfriend he broke up with, the one who made him want to be a bachelor. They had been on and off like Adrien and I, finally he drew a line in the sand, then she wanted him more than ever, but it was too late.

We pass a shop I love called *Les Petits Mecs* with awkward little plastic boys posing in tuxedos and then we arrive at Kiki's tree. It takes him a minute to see it past the trucks and buses. I catch a certain look in his eye.

'Did you guys sleep together?'

He smiles.

'For how long?'

'Not long.' He was never leaving Melbourne nor she Sydney. It happened after she returned from Paris, lasted a few months. I feel a mixture of intrigue, titillation, jealousy. It makes sense now why she knew so much about how well he kissed, how good he was in bed. It was kind of her to share him.

'Would you have stayed together if you lived in the same state?'

'I don't think so,' he says. 'We were better as friends.'

'Was it hot?'

He laughs. 'It was Kiki. Of course it was hot.'

'Can I take a photo of us in front of the tree and send it to her?'

I snap us, smiling in the street. You can see a section of the tree behind us and part of our heads. Kiki writes straight back: *You're in PARIS? I'm confuuuused. Ps. Hot couple.*

We continue on, down the rue du Château-d'Eau, spicy African food hitting our nostrils. A Molière is showing at the Porte Saint-Martin and I tell M the story of his death. M says he used to cut out the weird deaths from the 'odd spot' in the paper. I tell him about Isadora and some of the other strange deaths I found in my research:

Death by politeness, when not wanting to leave table to pee during long banquet and contracting kidney infection.

Death by falling as pallbearer and being squashed by the coffin.

Death by plastic bottle cap.

Death by forgotten parachute – classic.

Death by unbreakable window, which, it turned out, was breakable.

Entire team struck by lightning. Opposing team unharmed.

Death by flung pear, by hockey puck, fold-up bed, somersault, flying fire hydrant, office chair, beaver, falling cow, falling poodle (named Catchy, who died too), atomic wedgie, cinema chair, beach umbrella in strong wind.

Death by hungry hippo. That happened to a friend of a friend of mine. Honeymoon on the Nile, a hippo literally jumped from the water and ate her friend's new husband. *Ate* him. It was unfathomable and she forgave us our shocked laughter, having predicted it.

M is more shocked that I laughed than at the actual death.

'How many people a year do you think die by falling pot plant?' I ask.

He looks up and around. 'A few I'd say.'

I lead him down the rue du Faubourg-Saint-Denis, the street abuzz, every step a different culture. M looks as dizzy as I did when I first walked down here. I point out the place to get coffee, buy Turkish kebabs, Indian thalis, big cheap tubs of authentic Greek yoghurt. We stop outside the blue door to the theatre school and I show him the small plaque you'd miss if you didn't know it was there.

'Can you believe they'll be previewing in Portugal in a week?' I ask.

'Lord help them.'

We continue down the street, past the triumphal archway and into the 2nd.

'Is it weird?' he asks. 'Being back?'

'A bit. But comforting. Like coming home.'

'This is a Paris I suspected existed but couldn't find.'

'This is a Paris that doesn't exist when you're 22 on a tourist visa.'

'Perhaps you get the Paris you deserve each time.'

'I got the Paris I deserved last time.'

'You definitely didn't deserve that.'

We stop to look in a darkened restaurant window where waiters are setting places for the evening's service.

'Will you take me to the place where the accident happened?' he asks.

'No.' I say. 'I'd rather imagine that entire arrondissement has been erased.'

'Makes sense,' he says. 'What about your friends? From the building?'

'They've moved,' I say. I don't know this at all, but it helps to imagine it – the place – them – disappeared, deleted, but in a good way, like on holiday.

We sit on a terrace and order two *Leffes*.

'And the hospital?' he asks. 'It must all feel like a dream.'

'It does.'

'Sorry if I'm pressing too much.'

'It's fine,' I say, but I don't elaborate. We watch the passing foot traffic, pointing out French people we'd like to be.

'By the way ...' he says, taking one of his pauses as our beers are placed in front of us. 'I hope you don't feel any pressure with me being here. You know I have my own plans.'

'I don't. I won't. It's just happened like this. It's cool we get to spend time in Paris together.'

'Good. I'm happy to be in Paris. And I've got my tennis pal. I can stay with him as long as I like.'

'Where is he?'

'Somewhere out near Roland-Garros, in the 15th.'

'The 15th!'

'Is that far?'

'It's the other side of Paris. Just stay at the Récollets, if you feel okay with that. The 15th is not the Paris you deserve.'

We walk all the way over to the left bank, wandering up the rue Mouffetard towards the Sorbonne. He stops outside a stone building with the words Young & Happy above the door in childish plastic shapes.

'The Old and Sad! I stayed here when I first came to Paris.'

'Oh, no.'

'I met an Irish guy in this hostel who busked. He taught me a few Dylan songs on his guitar. I immediately wanted to give up tennis and stay here in Paris.'

'Did you?'

'No, I couldn't afford to. But when I went home I swapped my racquet for a guitar.'

'And you never went back?' I ask. 'To tennis?'

'Never.'

'And you never missed it?'

'Never.'

'So, you were just warming up for music all along. You just had to flip the racquet the other way.'

'Ha, yeah. Maybe.'

'And you didn't come back to Paris?'

'No. But I always wanted to.'

In the Luxembourg Gardens he buys me an ice cream and a crepe for himself. The sun is hot so we walk beneath the trees and back down towards Saint-Germain. My feet are sore now and my head is pounding from the concrete, my neck itching from the scarf. But I want to keep walking, so we walk all the way down the Boul'Mich', across the river and through the Marais to République. Répu. I tell M how I'd been calling it 'Répub' forever, thinking I was cool, but that Marie-France recently whispered to me that the locals say 'Répu'. *Re-puh*, says M, mimicking my accent well with the difficult 'u' vowel sound that requires your lips to be pouted right up, something Australians have a lot of trouble with. He is not embarrassed to put his face in unfamiliar shapes or try new sounds and I suggest to him it must be because he's a musician that he can mimic sounds so well. He agrees. Also he wants to get it right. We head for my favourite little bookshop just off the canal, which is like a naughty boy's bedroom full of dusty books and graphic novels and comics and posters stuck to the ceiling and walls, with an old man, the owner, always hidden behind stacks of books. Everything is in French but M and I spend a while picking up books, showing each other funny pages, rude drawings.

I find a strange box with a grotesque Alice with an oversized head painted on the front and a title I can't translate, something to do with Alice eating the moon.

I try to translate the blurb on the back. *In a nightmarish city, strange protagonists cross Alice's path. The young girl attracts them to her place then decapitates them. A failed artist falls in love with her – but hasn't he dreamed all this? Like a Bosch painting, animals, objects and men collide to give birth to a hybrid world, a tentacular city haunted to madness by solitude and desire.*

Inside the box is a series of hand-painted tarot cards with ugly, porny characters on them and a hardback porny Alice book with graphic scenes of lumpy dicks and decapitated heads, sad faces, pimples and chocolate, swirling animals and floating objects. It's so intricate I think it must cost a fortune, but when I look at the back it's only 20 euros. I show it to M, who gets a fright looking at one of the pages with Alice jerking off a crusty guy's dick. He takes it, smiling, and buys it for me.

'Thanks!'

I buy him the book on trumpets he was looking at that he didn't necessarily want. It's late now and we're ravenous so I take him for a *bobun spécial* at Le Cambodge and then, after dropping into Harry's on the rue de Marseille to collect Betty Bike (and introduce M who Harry immediately seems to have known his whole life) we walk back to the Récollets. I show him the lawn out the front where I used to practise acrobatics and lead him through the arcades to the private stone courtyard and café, and behind a secret gate and up the out-of-bounds staircase that has never been fully renovated since the 'Angels of the Récollets' squatted here in the early 1990s, plastering the crumbling walls in graffiti. You can feel people died here. You can feel people died everywhere in the Récollets, from monks to soldiers to artists. People died in the laundry, they died in the *cave* where we had planned to refresh Martha before it went on in Paris. Marie-France emailed me to say that wouldn't happen now, Martha is now someone else. I must forget about it, come to see it in Paris if I liked, she said, but to let it go. This hurt, but I know it's right.

The American Writer is smoking at the window as we approach our door.

'Jayne! Hi!'

'You're still here! This is my friend M. He's a musician,' I add. 'Hope we don't make too much noise.'

'How funny,' he says, 'that you were on one side of me, now the other.'

On one side of him with Adrien, now on the other with M. The American Writer, the mirror that I've stepped through.

⁓

I wake the next morning to the sound of M moving quietly around downstairs. I peer over the ledge and see him standing at the window looking out at the view so familiar to me. The tall *marronniers* are at their fullest; their thick, vibrant leaves blocking the view of the canal in the distance, but the playground and gardens and people below are clearly visible. I remember standing for days watching as he is now when I first moved in. His shoulders are down, like a boy. He stands still for a while, then goes to open the window but the heavy handle makes a loud squeak when he turns it which alarms him and he turns.

'*Chérie!*', he says. 'You're awake!'

It's funny how he says *chérie*, both the way he can't roll his 'r' and the fact he's using such a term of endearment so early. Perhaps he means *sweetheart*, in the way he's said a few times, which in English is playful and light. *Chérie* is more intimate, like we've been married for years, or I'm his daughter. *Ma chérie* is another thing entirely and belongs utterly to the world of Adrien, possessive, intense. I hope he doesn't call me that.

He has been out and bought pastries and made coffee in the saucepan. The coffee tastes better than at most of the cafés around here. I stuff a jammy croissant into my mouth and make a raft of pillows to prop up my neck on the hard bed as M goes downstairs and pulls his guitar out, playing a few notes to check if it's survived the journey. I hear the muffled sound of his recordings in headphones and call to him to take them out and play the music on the speakers. I lie and listen to the songs, which are close to finished now. They are all instrumental except one that a friend from New York has sung lyrics for and a theme has emerged based loosely around Dylan Thomas's *Under Milk Wood*; each song a part of a trip through a night-time town full of sleeping or dead characters, with weird interludes such as conversations and bells and toy pianos that sound like you're hearing them through doorways and windows like secrets. The opening track called 'Confessional' has an old recording of Richard Burton reading the opening lines of the play … *Time passes. Come closer now* … his voice distant, muffled by M's music. The whole thing is theatrical and strange, and M's job now is to put the songs in order and mix in all the pieces his friends have sent him to add to the tracks, a trumpet line, the vocals on that one song, a cello, a vibraphone melody.

I stay on the raft of pillows and drink endless coffee and call out thoughts on the songs and their order, which mostly don't work, but M tries them all. My favourite song called 'Bakehouse Blues' cannot seem to find its place on the album at all, while the others of their own volition start to settle into place.

'I have another idea,' I tell him in the afternoon as we walk down the rue des Récollets to find food. 'I've been thinking about it since yesterday.'

'*Oui madame?*'

'*Mademoiselle.*'

'Sorry. *Mademoiselle.*'

'We should be in Portugal right now, in the fires of hell. We have this bit of bonus time, right?'

'Yes.'

'We're sort of in purgatory.'

'Yes.'

'And a bit beaten up.'

'Yes. Especially you.'

'Especially me, but you too.'

'Maybe but not really.'

'*Anyway*, what I'm thinking is this. Why don't we use the summer as a sort of creative hiatus? I won't try and look for work and a place and all that, I won't tell my teaching clients or Daphné I'm back, and we won't worry about you and New York or going to Roland-Garros Siberia with your tennis mate.'

'Yes …'

'I want to write another play, something fun that gets the bad taste of Portugal out of my mouth. I could do a reading in the *cave*, invite The American Writer and some friends. You could work here on your album, you could even do some small shows here, we could imagine there's no future and just have these weeks of total creativity. When do you ever get an opportunity like this? The rent for July is paid, we can split the rest. Then after August, you can go to New York and I'll move out. But for the rest of summer we do a Hotel Amour. Just be here and forget the future.'

'Interesting.'

'Yes?'

'I love it.'

If we're careful, our money should last until the end of summer and I should still get a small amount of money from the play and M from his payout from his Australian job. M is excited to work here on the album and as soon as we get back to the room he starts looking up music shops to buy a special keyboard to help with his mixing. I unpack my clothes, wondering how I've ended up back here. I have no clue what I'll make a play about but decide I'll set a date with Chantal so I have something to work towards.

⁓

The next morning M goes off to Pigalle and I arrange to meet Nadine at Chez Prune. She is already there when I arrive, at a table in the perfect dappled sunlight. When she sees me she smiles and says, Ah, theatre. I know, I know, I say and order a *crème sans mousse*. She has adopted an *allongée avec pot de lait (chaud) à côté* at Prune. A long black coffee with a little pot of warmed milk beside it, so she can control the amount she puts in. Is that the same as a *noisette allongée?* I ask her. No, she says, putting her hand on my forearm and asking about Portugal. She can't believe it, though she can. You must have been so *alone.*

'Yes. But luckily my friend M came to do the sound,' I say. 'Kept me sane.'

'I didn't know a sane person was coming. Who is he?'

'A guy from Melbourne. A musician.'

'And you left him there with the savages?'

'No, he came to Paris. He's staying with me in the Récollets.'

She tilts her head at me.

'We're friends.'

'*Friends?*'

I try not to smile.

'I can't believe you didn't tell me you'd made a *friend.*'

'I hadn't, until a minute ago.'

'I'm confused. You invited this guy to Portugal? You knew him from home?'

'I actually met him through Kiki, at Dad's.'

'How did you make a *friend* when you were at your *dad's* in a *neck brace?*'

I tell her the story and she listens intently. 'And now you *live together?*'

'No, he's going to New York once the show is over in August.'

'Ah, New York,' she says. 'Now I get it.'

'It's not like that. I really want to visit New York.'

'Right,' she says.

I change the subject, asking if she has any ideas for me to write a play about. She says if she did why would she give them to me. I tell her how excited I am to stay in the Récollets for the whole summer and make stuff on my own and not be in the theatre. But it gets so hot, she says. Didier is taking her to Naples to ride around on motorbikes and go to Ischia perhaps, or Sardinia. She asks if we'll come and I say I can't afford it but I also just want to stay and work. Just don't jump in the canal, she says, remembering the day Harry got so hot he went for a slimy swim. Before she leaves she tells me Adrien is in Costa Rica now with Caterina, but they're on the rocks. I tell her I don't need to know. 'I know,' she says, 'but I'm sure it helps you to know you're not going to bump into him any time soon.' It does. Though his omnipresence has definitely started to fade.

She mounts her bike and rides off, like a character from the Nouvelle Vague. I head back to the Récollets with the empty feeling of wanting to start something but not knowing where to begin. I want to make something new and I also want to do nothing. I'm exhausted from Portugal, the move back here, the hard and soft beds, but I need to keep my mind occupied. I want to prove to myself that I can write a play, something that lives off the page. Something fun. Something weird. Something that will show the girls and myself – and M – I'm not weak.

M is already back in the room, new digital keyboard plugged into his laptop. He looks merry as he works, sipping coffee. On his way home he recorded lots of sounds, the traffic around the Gare de l'Est, the kids playing in the park. He tells me doing nothing is a fine project – true it might make for a difficult play (though look at Beckett) – and that in the act of doing nothing (especially if it's an active nothing) something might come, ideas for the book or the play, but if nothing comes then that's fine too. His plan is to sit with coffee and the curtains shut and give Bakehouse Blues one last shot, and listen to every sound over and over and correct any final blips before sending it to the Master.

'Who's the Master?'

He laughs. 'I said *to be mastered*. Mastering puts the final "puff"' – he makes a gesture with his hands, blowing air softly through his fingers – 'of air in the album. It's what makes it feel finished. You can't necessarily hear it, but you can feel the difference.'

I try and equate this with theatre but can't. Wish a Master could have come and breathed a puff of air into Martha.

He has a name, he thinks, for both the new band and the album, do I want to hear them? Of course, I tell him. For the band name he's wondering about Bombazine Black. As in, *hymning in bonnet and brooch and bombazine black*, from *Under Milk Wood*. It's an old mourning fabric. I love it, I say. I think. I need a moment with it. And the album name? *Here Their Dreams*. As in *from where you are, you can hear their dreams*, also from *Under Milk Wood*. A lot of *Under Milk Wood*, he says, sheepishly. Why so into that, I ask him. He says he's not sure. He just loves it. It somehow worked its way into the music and has now taken over the whole thing. I love it, I say. I love the use of 'Here' instead of 'Hear', as in, presenting 'their' dreams. And that's exactly what the album feels like, passing through people's dreams. He is pleased. And I do like Bombazine Black, I tell him. It's heavy, and sounds a bit metal, but there is something intriguing about it, especially alongside the music.

I don't know what to do with myself so I leave M to his fiddling and head back out and walk. Past galleries, *brocantes*, a stuffed animal shop. I buy a pair of spongey shoes from Tati that break the impact of the concrete. In a junk shop along the *quai* near Saint-Germain-des-Prés I come across a pile of old French magazines. '*Huit euros le tout*,' says the old man so I buy the lot and carry it in a Carrefour bag to the métro and back to the Récollets, setting up at the long table on the first floor to look at the articles on boiled food preparation and ads for soap and stockings. The women are smiling and I have the urge to mutilate them, so I go down to the Office Depot on Magenta and get a Stanley knife, a few canvas boards and acrylic paint and start cutting into the heads, removing eyeballs and teeth, defacing them like I would the faces of a newspaper with pen at home, infuriating my dad. The women are loving it, their heads tilting back dangerously, hanging by a thread; they're laughing so hard their jaws split apart and a shark comes out. A little boy with a pair of ladies' legs is on the telephone, saying, '*Moi aussi j'ai choisi.*' His mother has the body of a tiger and jelly cakes for eyes. It makes me laugh as I curl and slice and splice, gluing the cut-outs to the canvas board and painting scenes behind them. I go upstairs to the room and grab the magazine I kept from the plane from Australia and combine the old French images and words with modern photos of sea and animals. I stay on the first floor until dinnertime. M doesn't find the work as funny as I do but says it looks like I found something in nothing.

Days go by immersed in our work, M in the minutiae of the album, me in nowhereland with the scissors and the magazines. I try to focus the ideas I find in the collages into something, but nothing comes. Nadine has given me a spread she cut out from *Madame Figaro* of Helmut Newton's haunting photos of women in prosthetics – including a model with a black bob, naked except for a neck brace and a full-leg cast, balancing herself with a cane in a sumptuous old hotel, and another model with curled 80s hair, also naked in a Paris room, wearing an old-fashioned back brace strikingly like mine with bars and fastenings across the front of her body, breasts exposed. I go out and fossick through old junk shops and markets, collecting things about heads – some old reproductions of Max Ernst's *La Femme 100 têtes*, which is a French play on words that doesn't work in English, 100 sounding like both one hundred – *cent* – and *sans* – without. The hundred-headed woman is also the woman with no head. I find a picture of Marie-Antoinette's head. I find an old book on Isadora Duncan, with an image of an actress playing her, red scarf dancing out behind the car as they take off, her face enraptured.

The images are interesting, but no words come. I can barely talk about the accident, let alone make a play about it. I give up that idea and go back to playing with glue. I have set a date in four weeks' time with Chantal to do the reading in the *cave*, which at first seemed like plenty of time, but now more than a week has passed and I still have nothing.

The Alice book is perhaps the problem. It goes everywhere with me. Looking through it keeps my mind in that freefall, boundaryless place between languages, where the brain has to take a backseat. The text is so dreamlike I can't grasp the meaning of the sentences, or even the names of the characters. The original language is already so poetic and loose there's no logic to attach my translation to, which leaves me floating in a void.

One morning, lost for inspiration I start painting a few random, nonsense sentences on the canvas inspired by the Alice world and text:

Eat more child, it's mild.
In times like these
When meat is rare
Even my true love
Will rejoice
In a good, fatty rabbit

I play with naming a few characters according to the way they look in the images, mixed in with my impressions of the words and whatever comes to mind:

Lone Man Lost in Solitude
Arseface
Halfman
The Black Cat
Psychopath
The Sly Cad
Meanvoice
Grandma
Alice Spectaculous

For fun, I give the characters some lines inspired by the text, in no way attempting to translate the actual lines because I can't. I realise they were written in German first, then translated into French. So there's already been a leap in logic there. What if I warped it into dreamlike English? If I suspend my brain and use only the original thoughts as inspiration, weird worlds might come out that have their own meaning, wholly my own.

LONE MAN LOST IN SOLITUDE:

In my bed
Lives solitude
I put the remainders into the night table
And hope they won't run rampant and try to escape

     Meanvoice says Killer Bob is finished
     Burned
     Poor guy

          Laughing
          The mad ones hurricane
          And join themselves together in a fist

   I would be well within reason to throw myself against the wall
   And
   To die

       Behind me
         A girl drinks her daily dose of thoughts

I'm grateful that my French isn't good enough to understand precisely what the original text is saying. Though I doubt any French person would understand them either.

I make up my own story. Alice and her sister Grace are making a house of cards. When the cards fall, Alice looks around and can't find Grace. She sets off through a nightscape to find her, through abandoned yards and train tracks and seedy bars and vast plains. My thoughts take off in random directions and instead of taming them or worrying about logic or questioning where they're leading me, I follow wherever they go, referring back to the book when I get lost and allowing what I see or read to inform the next move or arrival of a character or bit of dialogue.

As the sun sets I run upstairs and fling open the door to 207.

'I've found something!'

M has earplugs in and doesn't hear me. I wait until the song ends, then wave the pages in front of him.

'I think I've found something.'

He takes out his earphones.

'What did you find?'

I tell him as we dress to go out and eat. He likes the sound of it. He's had a busy day too and we're both starving, so I plan to take him to the secret butcher's joint on the boulevard de Magenta, one of the best places to eat steak in the city, and ridiculously cheap. We're waiting for the lift when The American Writer's son arrives to wait with us. He looks just the same with his longish blond hair and cherubic face. Somehow in the two years I lived here I never had a single conversation with him. He gives us a weak smile.

JAYNE:

Hi, I'm Jayne. I used to live in 205 next to you. This is M.

The boy introduces himself but I don't catch his name, it sounded like Pam. Or was it Pan or maybe Johann? I want it to be Pam. He has a slight Nordic accent, which is interesting considering The American Writer has a Californian drawl, but people here have parents from everywhere. The lift arrives and we step in.

JAYNE:

It's so cool you're still here. It must be fun living in Paris with your dad.

M shifts his weight.

PAM:

He's not my *father*. He's my friend.

Pam steps out of the lift and we say goodnight and let him walk on ahead of us, out of sight.

'Kill me ...'

M laughs. 'Why would you assume it was his son?'

'I don't *know*,' I moan, 'he was so *young* when he first came here. Well, he looked young. I didn't think for a second!'

I lead M across the Gare de l'Est to the butcher joint. Though M was vegetarian through his 20s, like me, in the past few years he's developed an occasional lust for flesh. I used to go to this restaurant with Adrien and Séverine, a shitty-looking place from the outside, rough and stained with nondescript red awnings and thick, ugly curtains, but inside, simple and elegant. The waiter remembers me and seats us near the window and I order *bavettes* for M and me. '*La cuisson?*' he asks, tapping his pen against his pad as M hesitates, '*Bien cuit, à point, saignant ...*'

'FRITES!' says M finally, making me laugh and forget my mortification over Pam. He laughs as hard as me when I tell him he's asked for his steak to be cooked CHIPS, as the waiter smiles tightly, still waiting for the answer.

'*À point*,' I tell the waiter. '*Avec frites.*' *À point* is the maximum you're allowed to have your steak cooked, I tell M – medium rare – if you ask for anything higher you're ousted from society.

'Who would ever order a steak cooked more than medium-rare?'

'My dad.'

'Oh yeah,' he smiles, remembering the dried-out roast Dad made us once.

M assures me he's feeling fine about Bakehouse Blues. This is how albums work, he says, they have their own life and you can't force things. The song will have its own journey. Perhaps it will become a bonus track or a single or perhaps it will just disappear – this happens a lot. But it's the best song on the album, I say. Maybe, he agrees, but that doesn't mean it belongs as part of the whole. It's important to let the album be what it wants to be, to keep out of its way, not force it.

I've never heard work spoken of in this way, as something with a life of its own.

'I'm taking this concept to the nth degree with the new play,' I tell him, as I sip my glass of red wine. 'I'm so far out of my own way I'm off the planet.'

'I think that's great. Who knows what will come.'

'I guess. But what if it is nothing?'

'Then it will be nothing.'

A young woman sits down near us, giving M a second look. I think he might look like a famous musician, someone you can't quite place.

'So you're happy with the order then?'

'Very happy. It's done.'

'Wow. Now what?'

'Now I send it to America to The Master. Then I do the artwork. Then I have an album.'

'Then what?'

'Get it pressed, decide if I'll just do CDs or vinyl too. Then I've got my friends in Brooklyn – we'll rehearse the songs over there, then arrange a tour of America to launch the album. Then we sell fifty million copies and I buy a house in the Greek islands, get fat, smoke weed ...'

'You don't smoke.'

'Yeah, but you get the picture.'

'Would you think about playing a show here?'

'I'd love to but I don't know the scene. I don't think there is one.'

'Of course there is!'

'Name a French rock band.'

'Daft Punk?'

'Exactly.'

'I guess. International bands are always coming through Paris on tour but I've never known much about the local scene.'

'I'm sure it exists,' he says, 'but it's nothing like the States.'

'Or Melbourne.'

'Yeah. Everyone in Melbourne's in a band.'

Our steaks arrive. 'Can I come and visit you in New York?'

'Of course you can,' M says.

'I'm a bridesmaid in LA next year – maybe I could come then.'

'That would work.'

His label in Australia loves the demos and has promised him a small advance. They have arranged for him to meet with their French rep in Paris, a guy called Franck. M says it's important to meet the reps face to face – when they know you personally they work harder to promote the music in their countries. Not that there's much point for such a tiny album, he says, but still, Franck sounds great and a lunch has been planned for the day after tomorrow. Would I go with him, to play translator?

'Sure,' I say. 'Does that mean a free lunch?'

Back at the Récollets, M looks up The American Writer and learns that he's a super-famous author of transgressive gay literature. I hate myself. Why had I never bothered to find out who he was? I could have been learning from him, asking him a thousand questions; I could have gone to his plays, read his books, discussed them with him after. That girl in 205 seems so young now, so stupid. She thought he was just an older intellectual with his pretty son. I wonder how many other thrilling people I have overlooked, thinking I knew who they were.

⁓

M and I are waiting outside a restaurant in the 5th for Franck. It's a fairly humble looking local *bistrot* but is only serving an expensive *formule* for lunch. M is sure Franck will pay but if not it will be a fair dent in our budgets. Ordering just a coffee would seem rude.

An old rocker-looking guy in a relaxed but well-cut suit comes hurrying up to the doorstep and apologises, he had an unexpected call. He ushers us in.

Franck is a lovely warm man who speaks perfect English. He recommends the *formule* – he comes here most days – and we order timidly and sit back, enjoying the atmosphere of the neighbourhood restaurant with all its convivial owners buzzing around, locals at the bar, the sound of the old orange juicer. Franck asks all about M's album and his plans for launching it. When M talks about New York, Franck asks if he's considered launching it in Paris instead.

'Seeing as you're already here. I like the demos and the album would go well here for film and television. You know of course how big the French film industry is, and better quality than Hollywood. There's demand for good music and good musicians. Have you thought about film and television?'

'Absolutely,' says M. 'That's what I had in mind when I started writing this album. I'd like to be more independent and – to be honest – actually make some money. I just hadn't thought about doing it in Paris.'

Franck says it's smart to diversify. He confirms that there's not much good experimental or indie rock here, so M would have an advantage. 'You can support the big bands when they come and do your own gigs. If you launch your album here I'll invite all the booking agents, press, film producers …'

M's face glows.

Franck continues. 'Moreover, you'll be unique here. In New York you'll be just another Aussie guy with a band.'

They discuss the industry over the delicious lunch of *rillettes* and *blanquette de veau* and a little *tarte fine aux pommes* to round it out with coffee. Then Franck says, 'Think about it and let me know if you decide to stay. You'd go well here.' He signals the waiter – takes the bill and signs for it before we can fake-protest.

We walk with Franck out into the sunshine and thank him. He gives M his card and says keep in touch. After he's gone M turns to look at me, eyebrows raised.

'Interesting,' I say.

'Let's not think about it for now,' he says. 'Keep the pact.'

I hold up my hand for an awkward fist-bump and we decide to walk all the way back, letting the city and Franck's words sink in.

The day M sends his album to the Master we celebrate with a *sandwich-mixte* and beers at Les Philosophes, then play table tennis in the park off the rue Vieille-du-Temple. There are cement tables dotted all around

Paris, so he bought us each a bat and a ball to keep in our bag so when we go out together or meet up we can have a hit. He is infuriating to play against – all the years as a sportsman have given him a competitiveness that does not allow him to play just for fun. He can't help picking out my weaknesses and hammering them. He knows, for example, that if he repeatedly hits it to my forehand, eventually I will get a surge of frustration and smash it, usually into his t-shirt or a tree or a grandma walking past. I didn't think I was competitive by nature, but his attitude makes me want to annihilate him, break his spirit. It does not look like this will ever happen. But it's impossible to give up.

He asks about the play and I tell him I've contacted the author in Germany and he doesn't mind at all that I'm inspired by his book and making a play. Nadine wants to play The Black Cat and we've had fun casting the other roles; she suggested the bookseller's daughter to play Alice, with her blonde curls and sweet voice, a weedy English guy from Gaulier for Lone Man Lost in Solitude, and a hot French guy from our agency to play Arseface. I put up a notice at Lecoq and the bookshop for the rest of the cast members. There are 24. This piece will be mad and abundant and alive, if nothing else, and I will direct it like buggery. I need to write watertight like a fist; leave no room for interpretation, no actors to come with their greedy hands and murder it all, stomp on its guts. I won't Beckett it, with his rigid rules and stage directions, but the words will be solid, vibrating on the page so strong they'll assert their presence.

'What will you do now the album's gone?' I ask as we walk through the Square du Temple, stopping at another table for me to seek a chance at redemption.

'I want to start putting together an acoustic show of the songs. But before that there's something else I want to do.'

'What's that?' I say, serving the ball.

'I want to visit the building.'

'Which building?

'*The* building.'

'Sophie's building you mean?' I catch the ball. 'Why?'

'To see how it happened.'

'Oh god, I can't.'

'You don't need to come.'

'You don't have to do that.'

'I want to. Your dad wants me to.'

The mention of my dad hits me in the guts. That he and M spent time together without me warms me in a surprising way, like we are family already. It also makes me feel odd. This has been discussed. Part of me doesn't like that but it's comforting that it's real to them too. They haven't forgotten it either.

'I always planned to,' he adds.

We finish the game in silence (he wins) and sit down at a cement table with a chess board painted on it.

'It's important to see the place, I think,' he says. 'Don't you?'

'I don't know.'

A pigeon scrabbles in the gravel near our feet. I trace the lines of the checkerboard with my finger.

'But how would you get in? I couldn't ask Sophie.'

'Don't you have the code?'

'Oh, yeah.'

Of course I want someone to go to the building. Of course I want someone to look at it and see if they think it's safe and if I'm insane and if it was imaginable that such a thing could happen to someone and how it did happen. Of course. There's a part of me that asks the same questions over and over each day. A larger part of me wants to find a way to just forget about it, ignore that it happened, delete the 20th arrondissement and anything that reminds me of it from my mind forever, and move on. *Why did you come back then?* I say to myself. *If you truly wanted to avoid it and move on, why didn't you stay in Australia? Or move to Spain? New York?* The curious part of me needs to understand what happened in order to lay it to rest. And in some way, I know the health part of me wants to as well. Mental and physical. I don't want to manifest some block inside myself through the denial of a nightmare that the scars on my face show really did happen. I cling to the scars.

If it were just the neck pain that nobody, including myself, could see, I might question whether I'd dreamt it and gone mad.

The next afternoon, after spending the morning working on the artwork for the album, M grabs a few things, gives me a kiss, and leaves. I feel like curling up in bed but it's too hard on my neck so I decide to go for a walk. I don't want to lie around thinking about the building anyway, waiting for M to come back, imagining him seeing it, discovering what a freak I am, seeing that I'm a crazy person for doing that to myself, *papillon fou*. I'm scared for him to go, scared for it to happen to him though I know nothing like that would ever happen to someone like him, he is far, far too sane and also he knows what happened to me so he'll be super careful. It must be okay for other people now, there must be barriers, higher banisters, a warning, at least, the stairwell lights made brighter, the lift altered to make at least a breath of sound on its descent. Imagine if they've done nothing. That would tell me everything. That it was seen as completely my fault, an anomaly, a freak move by a young madwoman on the stairwell, an *Australienne*, an idiot.

I walk to Répu and stare at umbrellas and suitcases for half an hour, taking chocolate brioche from the Monop' to the Square du Temple. There's a bookshop with an English section on the other side of the park and I manage to procure a book by The American Writer and sit on the grass devouring it as I lick chocolate from the inside of the pastry. The writing makes my jaw drop. I had imagined the willowy, professorial-looking man penning elegant plays and books with deft and pleasant turns of phrase. In fact his writing is visceral, painful, full of life and blood and graphic sex. I've never read anything like it. I reprimand myself again for all the time I've lost with this master next door.

M is not back when I return to the Récollets. I read for a bit then stand in the window watching the children play in the park, a row of Afghan men with golden skin and green eyes sitting evenly spaced on a bench. They sleep in the park now because in summer the gates are open all night, then throw their sleeping bags and belongings in the trees during the day. I always wonder how they get them down.

Three kids race up a rope net, a toddler steals a bigger kid's ball. A couple of teenagers hold hands on a seat partly obscured by bushes. Though they have their back to me I can see it's a new relationship in the way their necks are held straight, their shoulders tilted slightly towards each other. They are watching something. A dog. The dog is a foil for what they really want to do.

Dinnertime comes and goes with M still not back. Now I feel sick. I sit at the round white table and try to distract myself by writing a few notes about the people outside and imagining their stories. Hurry up, M. The longer he's out there, the longer I feel he's gathering evidence that I'm crazy, he is sitting there right now on the stairwell, head in his hands thinking – but how did she *do* it? He can't even see how a head could fit over there let alone how I managed it. The lift, loud and beeping on its descent, lit brightly so you can see it coming, the banister high – so high she must have climbed right up on it and stuck her head out to achieve such an act. He is running, running away, calling the police 'This woman is crazy, suicidal, lock her up, she could do it again.'

I get out the play and try to read what I've written but the words look stupid and I have to fight the urge to scratch at them with a pen and throw them out the window. I put them away and walk around the studio, boil some water, curl up on a plastic chair. I turn the lights off, switch on the desk lamp, waiting, waiting, Marie-Antoinette.

It's late by the time M returns. He enters quietly in case I'm sleeping, then sees me and comes and sits at the table. The dim light of the lamp illuminates one side of his face, making him look like someone else.

'How was it?' I ask.

One of his pauses.

'I can't believe you survived,' he finally says. 'It's a death trap.'

I breathe out. Thank God. Thank God I'm not nuts. Then I feel guilty. I'm *glad* it's so dangerous?

'Are there stains?' I ask.

'Nothing at all. No sign anything has happened. Though the carpet is red.'

'What about the lift itself? Is it noisy? Was I wrong?'

'It's absolutely silent. Horrifyingly silent. It moves up and down without warning right in the middle there, just inside the rail. When I arrived it wasn't even dark outside and it was still impossible to know it was coming.'

Vomit rises. I focus on breathing. *In for four, hold for seven ...*

'The well in the middle is invisible even when there's a bit of light,' M goes on. 'By night time, when you were there, it's just – like the lift is not there. You can't see the pulleys or weights or anything; the lift has this cable system – you can't see any of that.'

'And the lights – are they still dim?'

'Completely. I could see how, when you were looking down, you would have seen Lou's face looking up, because she would have been close to the stairwell lights, which are pointed downwards. I could see exactly how it happened. How easily it happened. I made some diagrams.' He looks at me. 'I think that's enough for now. Let's sleep on this and talk more tomorrow.'

'No. I'm fine. I need to see.'

He pulls out his journal and shows me the measurements he's taken. 'You're 178 centimetres tall, and in the boots you must have been at least 182. The angle from stair five, when you leant diagonally across the banister, would have been around a metre, I estimate. It's too easy to do what you did. I just can't believe it hasn't happened before. It could certainly happen again.'

I notice the camera at his side. 'Did you take photos?'

'Oh. I think it's better —'

'Please, I need to see.'

We scroll through them. Outside of the building / Foyer with intricate black iron lift cage / Stairwell / Metal grill / Stairwell lamps / Red carpeted stairs / Sharp edges, darkness, angles / Sophie's front door / Doorbell / View of lift well from staircase / Shots of the lift from below ...

'Wait, go back.'

Something catches my eye on a photo of the bottom corner of the lift. The shot is taken from the stairwell with a flash. The flash has illuminated a strange object.

'What is that?'

He zooms in.

A clump of blood-caked blond hair attached to a small, dried piece of flesh, hanging from the bottom of the lift.

i am flying

        out over the stairwell
           in slow motion

     and the motifs from the Turkish carpet
       below
           are lifting from their velvety bed to join me

    i want to touch the pretty patterns
    but when my hand gets close
    they retreat
    and float away

Adrien is on my left and mum is on my right
    i can feel them but not see them.

                               Mum is gone.

        Adrien's hand is near mine
           i move to feel it but now he's gone too
          i'm alone with the patterns that sizzle and fade

it's dark.

    Lou's pale face is in the distance
bright like the moon

      i am drawn towards the face
         the face is mesmerising
      i have to touch the face

         the face is pulling away

the face is now a pin prick

now it's gone.

    sadness fills my body

    a voice backstage:

        Mademoiselle?

Oh God. I think I just died.

It's okay, it was a good life. People should most certainly not feel sorry for me, for I felt nothing but the roar. It's far worse to watch, than for it to happen to you, believe me, I know that now for sure. It's totally fine. I really am totally fine.

I'll just lie here now.

God it feels good to lie here. God it feels good to be dead.

They will pick me up and put me in the box and put the box in the oven like Mum. But I don't want to be cremated. Did I tell anyone that? *Merde.* I want to be buried! Let my bones fall away into the ground, take up valuable space. Will I break down? Will I pollute the earth with my skin with too many products in it and my hair with dye? Am I so full of preservatives that I will just stay like this, a plastic cup for all eternity?

Burial! Not cremation. Here in Paris. A funeral. Not a *celebration of life*. Black, black, a trail of mourners like Édith Piaf, a curved piece of stone like Oscar Wilde. The wails, the waste, the waste, all that life to be lived, all that potential.

God it feels good to lie here.

God it feels good to be the baby again.

God I'm lazy.

God it's a relief not to have to *be* any more. It's so tiring, being. You have to be, all the time. Constant being. I am enjoying this dark, it's warm and I don't have to be anyone or anything, just, dead.

Oh God, I think I died badly.

I think my body is on the second floor and my head is on the *rez-de-chaussée.*

102

God, I hope my head is not off. I hope nobody has to find my head. I hope my family doesn't have to live with that image for the rest of their lives. I hope Lou doesn't find my head down there. I hope she doesn't find my body.

I have seen horror but not man-made. I would rather have my head ripped off than see someone else die. Is that selfish? There are sirens, footsteps, a voice saying *Mademoiselle?*, but I'm far away, I'm not dreaming, the trick is to open my eyes but at this point I can't feel where my eyes actually are let alone how to operate them.

There is an angel at my bed. She sings, in a lilting soprano:

'If zero was no pain and ten was the most excruciating pain imaginable, what is your pain?'

'Three,' I sing back to her. She smiles. 'Very good.'

People talk around me, sweet voices, a jab in my *cuisse*, heaven. Love floods through me. The angel sweeps me up like a gust of air and travels me through the luminous halls. We enter a room filled with sunshine. A hundred perfect people in white are waiting for me. They are laughing and smiling and their laughter is the tinkling of piano keys. It's a festival, the festival of me. They are so clean, so bright, so perfectly in sync as they sing their angelic notes. I smile back at them as they gaze at me with love. They dance in perfect choreography towards the trolley on which I lie and each take their tiny piece of the sheet below me, lifting my feathery body from the trolley into a soft, fluffy white bed, drifts of sherbet all around. They each whirl past me whispering loving nothingnesses and float out of the room, leaving me in my perfect bed. The sheets are cool and soft, the sky outside is muted grey and it is going to be a glorious solemn day.

There is a witch at my bed. She croaks.

IF ZERO WAS NO PAIN —

Twelve! My jaw is clenched. The room is cold. It is not day yet. The woman is grey. My angel! Her skin is rough and pocked, her eyeballs yellow, her breath stale milk. She stifles a cough and looks closely at my face, in one eye and then the other, as if to check I'm telling the truth. She hobbles out.

Dead of night, the pain is approaching like a truck on a highway, I know I need to get out of its way quickly. Press the buzzer, the nurse is kind, her hair in cornrows, her teeth white in the dim light, her skin shiny like a chocolate ball. She pats my arm and gives me more Love, her name is Noémie, Noémie is in my head as I lie in ecstasy.

Dad? Mum?

Friends at the foot of my bed. They sit, reading my face, solemn, if I lie still, I might catch the way they're looking at me.

Mademoiselle TOOTLE?

Upstage left, no downstage left …

Prick.

     Curtain.

          Applause.

Mademoiselle?

Comment ça va?

A man is at the side of my bed. His face is meaty. It's the most beautiful meaty face I have ever seen. I want to caress it, but even just looking at it is satisfying. There are a million tiny holes in his meat face. His eyes sparkle in their lumpy beds. His hand is so kind, it sits on his hip and has a ring on it with a lovely black stone. How sublime. I bet he has kids. I love them too, with all my heart, the sweeties.

He takes out a measuring tape and lets one end fall to the ground. Two radiant younger men are there. They gather around me.

'We now will measure,' says the sweet fleshy man. God, my French is good. Bless university. Bless Lecoq. Bless Adrien. Bless Napoleon. I think about France and all its majesty. This bed for example, what a triumph. So well-shaped. So apt. Perfectly supportive without being hard. The walls – a lovely dove grey. The roof – porcelain white. The windows – steel-framed doorways to another realm – all those people in their wonderful lives, having parties and drinking coffee.

Being measured is ecstatic. This body. This heavenly blood pumping through it. I don't care if this is my life now forever. With every beat of my heart the Love flows stronger. The men move around me, patting parts of my exquisite frame with their soft fingers. A younger man wraps the tape around my forehead. Sparkles ripple through me. The meat-faced man shakes his head sternly at the protégé: *You must not get behind. Just take it as far as you can around the head. We'll estimate the rest.*

I wish the men would never leave, but they do. That's okay too, because I get to lie peacefully, and breathe air, and look at the window, approaching night – or is it morning – and listen to the glorious sound of banging plates and tin.

It is forever afternoon.

He is coming.

He will lean over me in his long black coat. He will smell of *Habit Rouge*. He will collect me in his big butcher hands, a tiny bird, *taille de guêpe*. He will smile. Mistinguett. La Miss. *Mon amour. Ma chérie.* He will not call me Jayne. He will never, ever, call me Jayne again.

A woman in a starched white uniform. Hair pulled back so tight her face is taut at the sides. A tray beside my bed – lunch. Do I want it? *Non merci.* She slams the contents into a plastic bag and with a furious glance at me, leaves.

Another incredible looking man, sitting beside my bed. He puts his hands on his thighs and bends over towards me. He says a whole lot of words that sound like soup coming out of a can, if the sound of soup coming out of a can were the loveliest sound you've ever heard. I understand a few things:

Minerva corset
   Ready on Monday
       Three to four months
       Spine
   Very important
       Hold the fracture in place
  See you on Monday then my name is Dr Belmondo

So much love. Adrien's hands, his hair. His lips. His smile. His hands on my body. My face in the crevice of his upper back as he sleeps. My fingers in his mouth. His black eyes full of tears. Mum's eyes. The safety of his arms. The way he says *ma chérie*. His shoes. His shoehorn. I love him. I love everyone. I love Paris. I love Sophie. I love banks.

I remember I was supposed to give an English lesson this morning to Pascal at Le Grizzly. Pascal is my favourite student; I go on Thursdays to the bank at La Défense and he takes me to the restaurant in a cement bunker called Le Grizzly and we laugh about the name of the restaurant and he asks me all kinds of questions about my life, deflecting any questions about his own, saying he's just a little grey man working with all the little grey men in the big grey building. Pascal is a rainbow. It's Thursday today, isn't it, I ask the nurse who comes to give me more Love. *Oui,* she says. I ask her the date. January 20. Can I please have the phone?

'Hello Pascal, it's Jayne. I am so sorry that I couldn't make it this morning – did you wait long?'

'Yes, but that's okay. Is everything alright?'

'I was in a funny accident! I got my head caught under an elevator and I fell down some stairs. I have a fracture in my spine, but it's fine, it's nothing. On Monday I will get a special brace fitted and I'll be back to work. Can we reschedule our meeting for Tuesday?'

Pascal is quiet.

'That is terrible Jayne. Do keep me informed. I am a little shocked. We will talk when you're out of the hospital and we can figure out a time then.'

I am suddenly worried about losing the teaching contract.

I call my boss and a few other students and Daphné. They all sound strange when I tell them what happened. Daphné says *mais là, t'es sérieuse?*

'You are very lucky. I am afraid!' says my student Williams Renaud, whose first name is actually Williams, with the S, it's not a typo. 'I don't think you'll be able to work on Wednesday somehow.' That's a funny thing to say. I am absolutely fine and once I'm out of here in the brace, things can go back to normal. Now I'll just rest a bit.

Dead of night. I have been stabbed in the neck and all the way down my back. Someone has ripped my cheek off. Somebody has put me in a vice and is slowly turning it to lift my head off from the rest of my body. I press the buzzer but the buzzer is not there. Where is the buzzer? I see it – it is on the table next to the bed. It is close but I cannot reach it.

Excusez-moi? I whisper, trying to raise my choked voice as loud as I can,

Excusez-moi?
Excusez-moi?
Excusez-moi?

Nobody comes.
The night and my tears never end.
A flutter and a bright light: snapped to consciousness from the deepest darkness.

Don't —

— sheets torn back. Fluoros screeching. Tepid water in a bucket. Gown off. Two robots from the future joined in military harmony on either sides of the bed. Chest washed as though there were never any breasts. Belly washed like there was never any food in it. Legs. Feet.

A scratchy towel follows the washer. The washer is lumped in my limp hand so I can wash my own nether regions. Thank goodness for hands being designed to come to groin level.

My body is rolled with professional gentleness onto its side. I howl in pain. The sheet is half pulled off from the part I have vacated, the new one geometrically centred where the old sheet was. My rear exposed to the open air. The carcass of me, rolled back to centre. Then on to the other side. I am weeping now. My butt washed down like a car. The sheet pulled through to the other side of the bed, taut as a rock. Me, back to centre, precise. I hold my neck still, body rigid. It feels good to be clean, at least. Pain ricochets from the top of my head down to my knees. I don't want to cry too hard because I don't want to upset the girl in the next bed. I push the buzzer.

'We're trying to bring you down,' says the nurse.

'I need Noémie,' I plead.

Noémie comes in with a group of nurses. They are all laughing and swearing like men on a wharf. Noémie is wheeling a stool and a bucket. Noémie! I need more Love! She nods and leaves the room. The other nurses stand at the end of my bed looking at me and continuing their chatter. The girl in the other bed stirs. Noémie is back with the stuff. She gives me a good, long injection.

I love you Noémie, I say, as solemnly and truthfully as I can, so she will understand. She pats my arm. Then she says the situation of my hair is *insupportable* and that she is going to wash it. I'm not scared because I have the Love now. A few moments ago that would have sent me off the edge. The blood caked in my hair and around my ears has begun to itch and though I'm not concerned about it, the thought of having a clean head isn't bad.

The procedure is complicated and involves them all shimmying me up the bed with great care so my hair can fall over the back of the bed. It takes forever and I don't think it's successful as they keep swearing but I lie back and enjoy the rush of the Love and think about making love with Adrien and with everyone I've done it with. The feeling isn't horny as much as an all-over sensation of extreme wellbeing.

The girl in the bed next door moves again – I can just make out the lump of her with my peripheral vision. Her mother isn't there. The girl starts to cry. The nurses ignore her.

'*Ça va?*' I ask. But it mustn't have been loud enough because she doesn't hear. I suppose my voice is still a whisper.

A day passes. Days.

'*Ça va?*' a woman asks. Opening my eyes hurts. The Love has worn off. That's the danger of sleeping too long.

'*Oui*,' I croak.

It's the mother of the girl next door. Her soft face is full of concern.

'What happened to you?'

'An accident.'

I don't have the strength to tell the story.

'I'm sorry.'

She looks over at her daughter who isn't moving in the bed next door.

'You know you're in the worst place. Poor girls. You fall into a strange category because you're neither post-op nor pre-op. And you're not ICU either. You're just recovering, but it's a bigger recovery than all the others who have had their operations. You get forgotten you two.'

I am in hell is where I am.

Perhaps that explains the placement of the buzzer just out of reach and the grumpy faces appearing around the door when I call.

The lady is one of those ones that talks without you asking any questions. I am grateful because I can't speak. But I want her to stay with me.

Black.

My hair is clean.

My hair is dry.

My jaw is clenched.

I want to kill.

Nadine is sitting at my side, her hand on my hand. She is calm. She is just calm enough that she is slipping under my radar of murder – her calm is winning – only just. The calm is washing over me, but not taking to my skin. It's sort of encapsulating me. It is keeping me quiet though inside I am screaming so loud this entire vast complex will turn to dust. Creatures made of tiny blades slip and slide through my veins, my skin is covered in icy prickles, but I am hot. I can't look at her – I look ahead. I want to kill, but I can't get up. A hot tear slips down my cheek. I feel Nadine respond but she is so wise and calm and *juste* she knows not to move. If she moved even a fraction right now, I would lose it.

It's the brace. And the lack of Love. There is still a little of it eking through me, but not enough to stave off the terrifying feeling of being locked in a prison the size of myself. I can't breathe. The brace is made of plastic, metal, and velcro. It goes from my hips to the top of my head – a flat piece of steel running from my mid-scalp down to the middle of my back. Bits of flat steel wrap around my waist and meet in another bit of flat steel that runs all the way up the centre of my stomach, with fabric adjusters that fasten with velcro in different stages up my ribs. They meet in a plastic cup part which fits under my chin and has a little knob which helps it be adjusted up or down – for eating, etc. A velcro strap fits across my forehead, keeping the back of the brace in place. I am part human, part machine – and the human part is rejecting the machine part and Noémie is not on and the Love is eking out and Nadine just reached forward to touch my hand and I want to kill the world, or die, let me die, please, let me die.

Stupid

M suggests contacting a Paris lawyer. The thought of giving the accident any more thought is dizzying but he is right, the stairwell is dangerous and how could they leave it like that and how can I not do anything? He says there could be compensation, for the medical bills, the flights, for Dad and Kate's having to care for me, for the pain and suffering and future loss of work. An impish thought pops up in a dark little place in me: maybe I can get some money from this. Maybe I can get three million bucks. Maybe I can be an artist forever and never have to teach English to men in banks ever again. Maybe I can buy an apartment in Paris, a big one with parquetry floors and tall windows, and be rich and have nice clothes and get facials and eat macarons every single day. Maybe that will all make the accident alright – maybe what I did was a clever ploy by my subconscious to shore me up for a glittering future. Maybe I'll be able to buy a house in Australia for visits and live here forever in opulence and luxury, travelling occasionally to Saint Barts or whatever that place was Adrien's friends always talked about.

M is good at this stuff because of his insurance job. He dealt with lawyers and lawsuits and compensation all day long so he knows how it works and he doesn't mind investigating it without me – he thinks it's at least important to talk to someone and see what they say.

The Australian Embassy gives him the names of two English-speaking lawyers in Paris: a young one who doesn't charge much but who you have to pay by the hour, and an expensive old one who does no-win-no-fee. M spends a long time on the phone with each of them. Both say essentially the same thing: This is not America. Do not do it for the money. Even if you win, there won't be much in it and they will make you work for every cent.

This news is harder to take than I expected. The idea of being rich had grown on me. I find myself crying, hard. It's embarrassing. Part of it was certainly the gilded dreams, but also it was about being seen, the immensity of the horror of the accident being acknowledged with a simple, very large cheque. *Sorry, here's what you deserve for that ghastly experience. Go buy yourself a lifetime of therapy. And a yacht.* The idea of being wrapped in wealth had lessened my fear of what the future might hold in terms of recovery and work. It had made me feel for a moment like I didn't deserve what had happened, like I wasn't responsible.

'They say the French system is hell,' continues M. 'Every cent you ask for has to be accounted for. It's not like America or Australia where they have public liability and set sums for *pretium doloris*, pain and suffering. The expenses for hospital bills, loss of income, Kate's flight, things like that, can be accounted for – as well as your projected future loss. The fancy lawyer says we could maybe build a case on this narrative, seeing as you just finished theatre school, showed promise, etc. But it's a long shot.'

'Sounds horrible.'

'It would be. You'd want to be sure about doing it.'

'Would you do it?'

'I don't know. It's so hard to know what you're experiencing.'

'But if you were me.'

'I'm not you.'

This hurts. *This wouldn't happen to me*, is what he's thinking. He quickly redresses himself.

'I probably would,' he says. 'I would need to know. See it, understand it. Force them to look at it.'

'So, you think I should do it.'

'I think you should do what feels right. Sorry to put it in your court but there's nothing I, or anyone, can do to advise you – you're the only one that knows what's right for you.'

'It would be so gross. And boring.'

'Yes, but sometimes you have to do boring things. If it drags on in your mind forever, that would be more boring than addressing it.'

'I don't want to carry this my whole life, wondering if I should have done it.'

'Exactly.'

Part of me does want to do it, money aside. Something in me has grown since M saw the building – I can't believe it's life as normal there, like nothing happened. If I'd died, got my head ripped off, would it still be just as it is now, with people going up and down those stairs as usual? What about little Lou? It could happen to her, or anyone.

'It would be smart to at least meet with one of the lawyers,' says M. 'Just to be clear exactly where you stand. It can't hurt. Do you think it might actually help you process the accident, at least, talking to someone about your case and what happened?'

I don't, and I don't like him implying that I need help. In Australia they made me see a psychiatrist and it made me feel like I actually was insane. I'm fine, I don't want to think about it, I just want to forget it and move on with my life. But that place is a hazard. Something in my core aches – that they've done nothing to make it safer implies they take no responsibility for the accident whatsoever.

I decide to meet the expensive lawyer. I couldn't afford the cheap one up front, so no-win-no-fee would be the only option. M offers to come with me, but I think I should go by myself. If I'm not strong enough to take a meeting about it then I'm certainly not strong enough to do the thing. M understands but warns me it may be heavy. We arrange that he will go and read in the Tuileries and I'll join him there afterwards.

The suites of Jonathan Hogarth are on the avenue Foch, near the métro George V. *Geor-jeuh sank.* On my way I pass a building I did an audition in once for a science-fiction film by a famous French philosopher/filmmaker about aliens and humans as animals. I was a cat waking up in an imaginary glass box, and the cat gets confused, then frightened, then angry, and the director kept yelling, '*Hungrier! Hungrier!*' at me and I couldn't figure out if he meant angrier or hungrier. Then I had to improvise and chat up a hot French actress, as though we were in a bar. I was so nervous and my French was so bad that my words came out from a strange place in my psyche: my mouth was speaking but my brain was somewhere else:

Do you, come, here?
Isn't this chair inside here, can you?
What is your sensation, of something?

Hogarth's lift is fancy, wide and fully enclosed. Sixth floor. It seems dramatic to take the stairs so I step inside. There's a safe feeling of opulence, spaciousness; the sheer weight of the construction. The metal gate jolts me when it clunks open outside the lawyer's door. I step gratefully out.

A velvet lounge in a long white marble corridor.

RECEPTIONIST:
Il n'en a pas pour longtemps.

I should run. Should I run? Squeeze the scarf.

JACQUES LECOQ:
An actor should see the sea in the métro.

MUM:
Get in there, you wimp!

The summer Mum got the rash, the water in the holiday town was cold as melted ice. She always jumped straight in. *You never regret a swim! Only having not swum.*

My name is called. My heart pounds. Just pretend it's a role, I tell myself.

INT: HOGARTH'S OFFICE – DAY
An opulent office the size of room 207 five times over. Heavy parquetry floors, ornate windows, sumptuous carpets, mouldings, lamps. A huge mahogany desk floats in the middle of the room, where a man sits hunched over a pile of papers. This is JONATHAN HOGARTH. He speaks with a booming British voice.

HOGARTH:
Pleased to meet you.

He stands to pump my hand. His wealth is reassuring. The long, ironed cuffs with silver links in the shape of bells, the wide silver wedding band, the heavy silver watch, the long fingers with the remnants of a tan. I bet he lives in Saint-Cloud, with a pool.

JAYNE:
(*quietly*)
Thanks for meeting with me.

He gestures for me to sit, then goes to the high windows that look out over the tree-lined avenue and starts pacing.

HOGARTH:
You know, I've seen a lot of stupid Australians. Tourists,
mainly. They come here, step off the bus, look the wrong
way, get hit by cars. Happens all the time. But this accident
of yours, I've never heard anything like it.

JAYNE:
(*swallowing*)
Right.

HOGARTH:
As I said to your husband, boyfriend, whatever he is, on the phone, there is no money in it. I'd take your case, which means nothing but a small fee up-front, but still. They don't cover suffering here – it's not America, Australia, every single euro must be accounted for and justified. A painful process. Perhaps you'd cover your costs and a bit more, if you're lucky – is it worth it? They're bastards, they'll make you cry. You've lived here a while now; you know the paperwork – do you? Do you really? You'll have to dress up and act sad and go on and on about your ruined career, your ruined face – let me look at it – yes, not that ruined, is it? You're alive, you're fine, you could still act, you can still do whatever you want. Honestly, if I were you, I'd get out of my office and never look back. Go on with your life, forget about all this.

JAYNE:
Thank you. I'm not sure if I can just move on as if nothing's happened. What about other people? What if the same thing happens to someone else?

HOGARTH:
This is Paris. It's a very particular city and this is a very particular accident. It's an old city and it has its own rules – you must know how dangerous so many things are here every day. You must know your case isn't going to make a lick of difference to the way things operate.

JAYNE:
It would make a difference to *me.*

Would it make a difference to me?

JAYNE:
What if I decide to go ahead with the suit?

Hogarth sighs, like his preliminary spiel is over and he's now moving to Phase 2.

HOGARTH:
Well, you'd have to put all those acting skills to use.
(*he rubs his chin*)
The life you have lost. Your career. No lipstick, bad clothes, you are ruined. Everything would have to be documented, you'd need to see psychiatrists, psychologists, doctors, and get them to say how badly you're suffering PTSD, you'll need to get your acting teachers and colleagues to write letters saying you were on the rise and that now you're ruined as your face can't express emotion and you're physically unable to use your body in the same way you did before. You'd have to act act act, ham it up for all these people and collect a big fat dossier for us to present to the court. Now, if you could convince them that you were the next ... Cate Blanchett
(*he paints her name in the sky*)
and now you're a hopeless case who is going to require care
for the rest of your life
(*he looks into the distance, gesturing dramatically*
with his perfect-suited arm)
a rising star, cut down in her prime, the number might look more like this.
(*he takes the paper and writes a number on it,*
then emphatically adds a large '0'.)
And you'd give me a third.

Paris is dangerous, of course I know that, I always knew that. Fire is another major threat here. Fire escapes are too ugly for the Paris landscape and that's why there's a *caserne* in every neighbourhood full of hot firemen waiting to be at your place seconds after the call. *Tant pis* if they can't get there quick enough and you're on the sixth floor. I don't want to portray myself as hopeless, with no future … I don't want to think of myself in that way, however bad the pain is now, however uncertain things are. It would be so nice to walk out of here and never look back.

I tell Mr Hogarth I'll think about it and he shakes my hand again and I leave, taking the stairs down all six floors, keeping well to the side, though there's nothing to be afraid of.

⁓

In the park I recount every moment of the meeting to M. There is a cool wind and he gives me his jacket to wear. We keep talking as we walk back towards the 10th through the Palais Royale, where I keep my head low to avoid the ghost of Adrien. When I ask M his opinion he says let's not try to decide yet, it's just good to have the data. He has said this before – about getting the data – it's something I'd never thought of. Let's just sit with the data for a bit.

We sit at Chartier at a table beside a mirror on my bad side, the scar lit up like an art display, and try to think of other things as we eat cheap *céleri rémoulade* and tomato salad and ham, marvelling at the plates of tripe and *andouillette* passing us. I tell M about the Bistrot 1929 near my old place in the rue de la Chine, how they served *andouillette* and other traditional French dishes in there, and how I'd always wanted to go but could never afford it. I dreamed of going to the Bistrot 1929. It was like something from an old French movie, with dim lights and old leather banquettes and menus on chalkboards. It was a long, deep space and there were always a lot of people inside of every age and demographic, and the menu changed every day, French dishes like *andouillette* and tongue and cassoulet. I tell M about Kate and I looking in the window one day after we'd been to a medical clinic to get my stitches removed. He asks what that was like, so I tell him about the nurse taking me into this red room, telling me to lie down on a stretcher and pulling a curtain around me while Kate waited outside. The room was like a cave, a sex dungeon, old exposed stone bricks painted mahogany red. It made me think of the inside of a body cavity, but I was super woozy on painkillers. The curtain was swept aside and a woman in a suit approached me with a case of metal implements, and my mind went back to that awful film about the perverted twin doctors who performed bizarre gynaecological procedures on women. M knows the one. I was worried the lady was going to make me pull my pants down, I always worry doctors are going to make me pull my pants down, even when I have a sore throat. Anyway, there she was above me, hand poised, she asked me to close my eyes and I did willingly. Then the strangest sensation. She *cut* the stitches from my face, one by one, thousandth after thousandth, and every stitch pulled and puckered, burning and stinging my face. *Il faut vraiment une lame?* I moaned. Why a razor? Wasn't there something that could snip instead of tug? For a decade I lay in that bloody cavern. She gave me a *fraise tagada* at the end, my favourite, which I sucked on as I snorted back tears and snot and Kate led me out into the street.

'Anyway – *andouillette*. A man was eating *andouillette* by the window that day. It looked like a long, curled shit. Kate and I watched as the man ate forkfuls of shit. Then I went home and passed out. The next day, Kate and I made a pact that we'd go to the Bistrot 1929 as soon as we could, and whichever of us ate *andouillette* would get their dinner paid for by the other. Which would have to be me, as I couldn't afford it. But being inside that place would be worth eating shit for. So, it was agreed.'

'What's in *andouillette*?'

'I think pig's colons. Or perhaps tripe. Intestines. Intestines stuffed into an intestine.'

'Yummy. Did you go back and eat it?'

'No.'

'We should go there and order it.'

'One day,' I say, knowing I won't. 'But you'll have to pay.'

Nadine thinks I should do the lawsuit. Harry's philosophy is to stay well away from any non-essential administrative procedure in France. Don't. Go. Near. Kate says definitely do it; she says they should pay for what it's cost me, and I say they should also pay for what it's cost her and Dad. Kate had to defer her university year, get time off her job and leave her new boyfriend behind to come over and play nurse to me. She says she doesn't want me to sue on her account, but I should sue. When I ask if she thinks Mum would say to do it, she says definitely. Dad is horrified about the current situation of the lift but says I should only do it if I feel capable, and to forget doing it for him or anyone else. Kiki says if I think I might regret not doing the lawsuit, then I should do it.

I know no one can decide for me, but I wish they could. Nobody I know has heard of anyone with a similar experience to share. I wish there was someone I could ask.

I think of Beckett's Winnie. What would she do? There in her mound of earth day after day, Beckett throwing stones at her. The relentless sun, the scorched grass, the solitude, the bells reminding her of the passage of time, her husband who is not incapacitated like she is. And yet she is happy. *Another happy day!* You could put Winnie's head in a guillotine and she'd say, 'Glorious!' She wouldn't waste time on justice, there is no justice, it's an illusion, life is just life, you can end it all with the revolver if you really want to.

I'm grateful to be alive. I remember a moment after I regained consciousness, experiencing a sublime feeling of the simple beating of my heart. I remember thinking, I don't know where I am or who I am or if I will ever move again, but if I am nothing more again than this piece of flesh with a beating heart, it is enough. The feeling of being nothing but alive. I remember Mum's last days, the way she drank murky soup through a straw, drawing on life, just one more moment. We watched her, pitying the pathetic excuse for life she was leading, in and out of consciousness, her bodily functions by that point mostly operated by machines. And yet she drew on the straw for more. I couldn't understand why she wanted more of this life. Now I understand. She was alive. The simple act of being alive is more than I knew.

And for all the pain and frustration of my recovery, I remember times at Dad's when I felt such an intense joy and sense of peace at being allowed to do nothing for three months. To stop. It felt like a gift to have a reason to opt completely out of life and feel what it was to simply exist. Four walls, somewhere soft to lie, a little food.

I know I'm lucky. I am the luckiest person in the world. I get to live. And well.

In Paris.

If I did go ahead with the lawsuit, what would I actually be suing? The very thing I love most about this city – its embracing of beauty at all costs, its refusal to become like anywhere else on earth. Can I sue beauty, sue thrill, sue complexity, sue cancer, sue death? Sue myself for being an idiot, for freaking my family out, for scarring Lou, and Sophie for life? Sue life itself?

No. I can't do it. It makes no sense. I'm fine. I'm here.

Paris Loves Us

As if rewarding us for not taking her to court, Paris goes out of her way to show us her gratitude.

First: Jean gives us a chicken.

I've been trying to earn Jean's respect since I began frequenting the rue Alibert markets on Sundays almost three years ago, initially not knowing what anything was called and having to point. He remembers me and perhaps senses something has changed, I'm not sure, but after M and I have filled our newly purchased cart with fruit and vegetables and I've paid, he gestures to me to come closer.

'*Vous voulez un animal?*'

I don't understand what he means. Do I want an animal?

'*Poulet, lièvre, canard ...*' he mutters in a low voice.

'*Euhh ... poulet?*'

He winks and asks us to come around the side of his stand, where he hands me a supermarket bag with a chicken in it the weight of a human head.

'*Cinq.*'

He makes a 'shh' gesture with his dirt-covered finger as we pass him the five euros and sneak away with the bag. There's a chicken seller at the market, and a butcher, so perhaps it's illegal for Jean to be selling his own meat.

M opens the bag in our sink at the Récollets to find a freshly killed whole chicken. De-feathered, but that's about it.

'This will be amazing,' he says.

We have to share it so I call Nadine and she says wow and can she bring Didier. Of course, I say, and they come over with a bottle of white wine and a big bag of cherries.

Nadine stops in the doorway. 'Hello!'

'Nadine, this is M. M, Nadine.'

She introduces Didier and I say 'Nice to meet you' in English, because there is no French way to express this informal, warm phrase and I've given up trying. He leans in and we kiss on both cheeks. He is a solid build with neat, understated clothes and a warmer, rounder face than the typical Parisian. He's originally from Bretagne but has lived in Paris since university. Nadine seems flushed, like she can't get her head on straight or wishes she'd worn something different, but after a glass of wine she's back to her old self and is asking her usual thousand questions and making her statements while M and Didier prepare the chicken.

'I really think you should do the lawsuit. It's insane what happened. Do you think you made the right call?'

'Will you stay here or move to the other room in the Récollets?'

'I have a lighter scarf you could wear instead of that heavy thing. It must make you so hot.'

'Do you still wear the scarf to sleep?'

'When does M leave for New York?'

'He seems nice ...'

I tell her about the new toaster oven we got for ten bucks from a guy that was leaving the Récollets, that looks like it might last one dinner.

'Even for this one dinner, it's worth it,' she says, sniffing the air and closing her eyes.

She's not mistaken. The flavour of this chicken is like nothing we've ever tasted, and Paris has good chickens. This must be what chickens tasted like when Mum was growing up in the country, I tell them as we sit around eating our portions with potatoes on the chipped residence plates. 'They each had a job on a Sunday: chase it, kill it, feather it, drain it, cook it.'

'No wonder you were vegetarian,' says Nadine.

'I was too,' says M. 'For a decade.'

'It's funny how we don't want to know how things die that we eat,' says Nadine, mouth full of chicken.

Didier speaks good English with a heavy accent, so we all speak in English, but Nadine and Didier speak together in French. It's intriguing to watch how different they are in the two languages – in French closer and more curt, in English, sweeter and more distant.

'Did you get the role in the touring play?' I ask Nadine.

'No,' she says, pouting. 'They gave it to some asshole from Lecoq.'

'Do I know them? I'll bash them for you.'

'Someone in first year now.'

'*Merde.*'

'What will you guys do next?' Nadine asks.

I tell her we've decided not to think about it yet, it's still summer and we're on art camp.

The 'we' vibrates.

'What are those?' asks Nadine, looking around the walls at the collages I've been making, a woman with a plane flying through her head over the Great Barrier Reef, an old statue pinching a woman with tits made out of canned meat.

'Just an attempt not to think. They helped me start writing the play.'

'Oh. I put your name down to do a reading at the English bookshop of your book.'

'Nadine!'

'It's ages away, but it fills up fast. You don't have to do it, but your name is down.'

Second: The fashion show.

I decide to personally hand The American Writer one of the posters I've been sticking up around the Récollets advertising the play reading in the *cave*. My hands tremble as I knock at his door. He takes a while to open. He looks dishevelled, surprised.

JAYNE:
Hi! I wanted to let you know, I've been reading your work –
finally – and I love it. I wish I had talked to you about it sooner.
I'm sorry. Also, I wanted to invite you to the reading of a
play I've written – down in the *sous-sol* on Friday. Here you
go – no pressure!

THE AMERICAN WRITER:
Thanks!

There's a twinkle in his eye. I'm a *dick*.

JAYNE:
And Pam too.

He looks confused.

THE AMERICAN WRITER:
You mean Carl?

JAYNE:
Oh yes, of course, Carl.

THE AMERICAN WRITER:
And we'll see you tomorrow night at the fashion thing
downstairs?

JAYNE:

The fashion thing?

THE AMERICAN WRITER:

There's a men's fashion show.

JAYNE:

I didn't know about it.

THE AMERICAN WRITER:

Oh, maybe we found out before you arrived back. We're all invited.

JAYNE:

Cool. Right. See you there.

That night I lie next to M watching his array of facial expressions as he reads a page of The American Writer's book. Wince. Nose screw. Eyebrow raise. Squint.

'No.' He puts the book down.

'Not for you?' I ask.

'Not for me. But that doesn't mean it's not great.'

'You're quite straight aren't you.'

'Not at all.'

'Yes, you are.'

'I didn't think I was until I started reading that.'

'I think you're very straight. On the gay-straight spectrum you'd be right up against straight.'

'That end of the spectrum would be right-wing extremist straight. I'm not that in any way. But I don't have any desire for cock.'

'None whatsoever? No cock curiosity?'

'Boring as it is to say, I've never had the curiosity.'

'And you don't like cock books.'

'I have nothing against them at all. It's the violence in this that gets me. And the sadness.'

I show him some of the pages from the Alice play.

'I love this.'

'But it's violent and sad, with cocks in it.'

'It's funny and weird.'

'Adrien thought I was dirty, and that the things I liked were *glauque*.'

'What's *gloook*?'

'You can guess, from the sound.'

'Dark, scary, uncomfortable?'

'I assume so.'

'Just because I don't love stories of teen cock and fisting doesn't mean I don't like dark and weird.'

'That's good.'

'Keep writing like this.'

'Thanks! I will.'

'You need to work on the structure though.'

'I know.'

'I'll help.'

The play is called *Alice Eat the Night Violet*. It makes no sense and is confusing to read but I like it that way and I don't want to question it. I want to trust my instincts and see where they land me, after second-guessing myself so much I disappeared.

⁓

The next evening, we get dressed up for our dinner date before the fashion show, which I've kept as a surprise. As a late birthday present, M's mum transferred him some money for a very nice dinner out in Paris. He suggested the Bistrot 1929 but I laughed it off, suggesting we go to Chez Julien on the rue du Faubourg-Saint-Denis. We can walk there, and it's delicious and not too pricey, though inside is like a fairyland with its *femmes-fleurs* and giant mirrors and green stained glass ceiling and twisting, twirling wood pylons and lifetime waiters in formal black and whites and crepes that get set on fire. And we can get dressed up all fancy and pretend we're in the Belle Époque. He has had his suit steamed at the *pressing* and I am wearing a big tulle skirt with embroidered flowers on it that Gabriella stole for me years ago and a t-shirt and boots and bright red lipstick and a thinner, stretchy red cotton scarf Nadine lent me that stops me sweltering in the pounding heat of the summer and feels like a gateway to letting it go.

M adores the dinner and we do the full *foie gras – champagne – steak-frites – bourgogne – tarte tatin – calvados* and feel like kings. M looks royal, jolly, and we walk back up the street merrily drunk.

Back at the Récollets the gates are firmly shut with serious bouncers on them. We explain that we're residents and the men ask to look at our badge then let us in. The architecture building has been turned into a high fashion runway with a jungle theme; bright lights swing around to highlight the coconut trees and ferns installed along the ancient stone walls and in the high chapel ceilings, as lanky men in colourful autumn wear sashay down the catwalk. I see The American Writer in the doorway smoking and watching the show, I see cocktails. M wants beer. When I return, he is standing beside a group of men with extreme hairdos and suits and shirts tailored right to their form. He watches the show with them, intrigued, as I slip the beer into his hand.

'Would you wear that?' I say when a man appears in a fluorescent orange tank top and skin-tight jeans with citrus fruits all over them.

'Definitely.'

'You're not as straight as I thought.'

As we watch in awe, a tall guy with a thick black coif wearing a neon-green suit with its collar up and a white cassette tape around his neck like a pendant approaches us. He gives M an unapologetic once over and says in thickly accented English, 'I like your costume.'

'I'm not in costume,' says M, looking down at his clothes.

I whisper to M, 'He means your suit.'

M says *merci* to the guy and looks back to the show.

But the guy isn't done with him. He bunches his hand into a ball and puts it beneath his chin, not taking his eyes off M. 'I like your pose.'

'I'm not posing,' says M.

'Of course you are,' says the guy.

I choke back a laugh. M's pose? He's standing there watching the fashion show like he's watching the cricket on a big screen at the pub. Beer in hand, other hand in pocket, one foot out, slight backward slouch.

I introduce us and we all do *bises*. The guy says his name is Mondrian or Montréal or Amandin or something. I think I'm going deaf. The music is loud. The cocktail is incredible.

'So,' he says, 'where you coming from?'

'Dinner,' says M. This sets me off.

'Australia,' I shout to Mondrian, telling M that Mondrian meant 'where are we from?' Mondrian is speaking English and yet I still have to translate. I'm concerned that we seem rude so I quickly ask Mondrian if he works in fashion, say aren't the cocktails great, does he live nearby. He pouts, putting his fist back beneath his chin and looking me up and down.

'Why are you wearing that scarf?'

'Why are you wearing a cassette tape?' I fire back, surprising myself.

Mondrian gives me a serious look. 'I don't mean that you should not wear a scarf. It is an intriguing look. But not this one you're wearing, it's very *moche*.'

He reaches into the oversized pure-white tote he's carrying and says, 'Here, girl,' pulling out a length of soft silk in a geometric design with vibrant pink, turquoise, red and white shards intersecting with one another. '*Je peux?*' He reaches out to unwrap the claggy cotton from around my neck and, as though understanding, rather than draping his design loosely around my neck, wraps it securely, tying it at the top with a small knot.

I'm not sure what to say other than *merci*. Mondrian steps back and admires me like an artwork. '*C'est bien comme ça.*'

I reach up to my neck to start unravelling it, but he puts his smooth hand on mine.

'*Nononon. C'est pour toi.*'

I need some air. M is talking now with Mondrian, so I go to the exit and bum a cigarette from a bouncer and stand in the Récollets courtyard smoking it, ignoring the image of the smoke polluting my neck and coming out my throat à la the old woman in *Beetlejuice*. I notice The American Writer sitting beneath the arcades, smoking. He looks over at me. I think of going to talk to him, but he seems so content in his solitude I don't want to break it. I wave to him and walk back to the party.

~○

Third: Martha is a piece of shit.

I choose to see this as a more complex manifestation of Paris's love, but love all the same. *Marthe Va Au Marché* comes to town and is playing at a theatre in the 19ᵗʰ. The girls returned a few days before it opened and Marie-France came rushing over to tell me how horrendous it was in Portugal and how worn out they all are and how they're all hanging on by a thread. They have six shows to do in Paris and Marie-France tells me to stay away.

'I have to see it,' I tell her.

'Do not come near.'

'But it's still my work in some way.'

'It is in no way your work. We all agreed to take your name off the program, it is too far now from anything you wrote or directed.'

This does not feel good, but I suppose it's a relief.

'I'll come to closing night,' I say. 'I'm too curious not to.'

Marie-France and M go out for a coffee to talk about the lights and staging, and the next day he leaves early to go and set up in the theatre. His face is war-ready. He comes home later in the day saying the piece is bizarre, he can't quite figure it out, but that he didn't pay too much attention, just gave the stage manager the music and lighting plan. He said the group looked exhausted, but they were all kind to him and asked after me. I think about contacting Faye, but I know the feeling of when you're in something and can't talk yet.

On closing night M and I head to the 19th. The theatre is a mid-size black box and it's far from full. We take seats towards the back and I find myself next to Claude, my favourite teacher from school. I love Claude. He is super old. I can't quite tell how old because he's so fit and has been teaching at Lecoq so long he seems fixed in time. I remember him introducing himself to us and saying that even though he'd taught at the school for a long time he knew nothing so don't ask him. He never got my name right.

CLAUDE:

Jenny! *Oh la la, ton histoire ... j'ai entendu ... ça va maintenant? c'est mieux?*

JAYNE:

Oui oui c'est rien. I'm completely healed – look!

I turn my head from side to side, it's stiff but it turns.

CLAUDE:

C'est affreux. We were worried about you. And you did the *saut de mains et tout!*

It had taken a year before I could do a handspring and Claude had pushed me to breaking point, shouting, 'Lazy!' when I choked out the words *'Je n'y arrive pas!'* from upside-down in a handstand, two people holding my legs. It just didn't seem physically possible to spring myself over. I was too in my head he said, and pointed the fact out to everyone in the class. I cried like a weakling, hating myself for my wet cheeks, choking back the tears as we moved onto cartwheels. *That* I could do.

The curtain goes up. The show is all manner of shite. Six women performing a series of scrubbed scenettes in a supermarket, using their bodies as well as they can, polishing a turd. There is no story, we can't understand what is happening, there is no sense of tragedy. Marie-France is subdued as the *coryphée*, we feel nothing but confused as we watch. '*Une soupe,*' Claude mutters beneath his breath, *Oh, merde.* He continues to click and sigh loudly, unafraid of being heard. He's never cared, he would huff and bury his head in his hands when we did a bad *autocours*, asking, 'Why? Why?'

They are lifting Faye up in a sort of ballet dream sequence when I manage to articulate in my mind what the piece is. It's *scholarly*. There is something profound missing from its centre – good writing. Writing is what takes a physical exercise and turns it into something meaningful. Writing is the source. The piece I had written wasn't strong enough; I had deliberately left holes in it for the girls to fill with their physical impulses, but more to the point, my writing wasn't compelling enough. And now it occurs to me that perhaps I hadn't completed the script partly out of laziness, and the awareness as I worked that it was really, really hard. I can see a bit clearer now what needs to be done, as I witness the void of a play with no script.

M has been telling me about *duende*, this idea Lorca spoke of about the dark little spark in live performance that gives you chills, tapping into the naughty, demonic part of your humanity. He has a dog-eared little book called *In Search of Duende*, in which *duende* is described as a sense of 'irrationality, earthiness, a heightened awareness of death, and a dash of the diabolical'. Like with the bouffon, the artist must not surrender to *duende*, it must be skilfully wielded in order to be imperceptible to the audience. They either feel it or they don't. Like when it's *juste.*

M read to me from the book: 'The *duende* is a demonic earth spirit who helps the artist see the limitations of intelligence, reminding him that "ants could eat him or that a great arsenic lobster could fall suddenly on his head"; who brings him face-to-face with death; and who helps him create memorable, spine-chilling art.' I copied this out and stuck it to the wall.

In music, *duende* is in the 'black sounds'. In an article M found online, a scholar named Jan Zwicky described it as 'the dark counterpoise to

Apollo's light, music in which we hear death sing … *Duende* lives in blue notes, in the break in a singer's voice, in the scrape of resined horsehair hitting sheep gut … we sense the gleam of the knife, we smell blood.'

I could hear the influence of this in the scratching, rasping sounds in M's guitar playing. Normally, he told me, the sounds of the fingers moving up the strings are cut out during mixing, but this time he has kept them in.

A group of people in the back row of the theatre start laughing and shouting – '*Non! Sors de la scène!* Get off! This stinks!' Perhaps they got free tickets. I can sense at this point that the actors want to give up, but they are so professional they double down, and this is funny. The people shouting are drunk – if they had tomatoes they'd throw them – and the dullness of the theatre, which is growing emptier, only makes their boisterous ranting resonate more. A sense of *duende* is in the room for a moment – the death of the show and the unapologetic childishness of the hecklers. Looking at Tez and the fire in her nostrils I can see that though this piece is a flop, the next thing these girls do will have *duende* for sure: they have touched death. If the Alice play has some *duende* in it, it will be because of my frustration with *Marta Vai ao Mercado*. You have to die first to find *duende*.

It's not a nice feeling to see a work flop so badly but it's an excellent lesson. A play needs a strong director and a strong writer. I hadn't pushed it through hard enough – sure, the girls hadn't helped, but they were confused. I wasn't clear enough with where I wanted the show to go. It's okay to have failed here, we are freshly out, we're learning, and I can imagine Jacques Lecoq nodding right now, saying, 'yes, yes, *c'est ça*. Don't be a fuckhead. You have disappeared up your own butts here – nobody in the audience can follow what's going on – where is the story, where is the *truth*? What are you trying to say? Don't think *too much*, don't get *coincée dans la tête*, but use your head a bit, someone's head, a little bit of head *quand même*.'

In the days after the show is over the girls contact me one by one. Marie-France comes to the Récollets moaning, her body heavy and her ankles thick; she brings chocolates and we eat the whole box. Faye comes with booze. Meg writes an email, Élodie sends a text message, Tez rings. Before Faye leaves for the States we meet up on the canal like in the old days and sit drinking cheap wine with a big moon until we're so drunk we can laugh about it all.

⁓

Fourth: M gets a Paris gig.

On the way home from the markets on Sunday – without a *poulet*, Jean hasn't offered again – we notice a bar called Chez Adel with live music playing. As we sit and drink an Amstel, a Latino guy strums a terrible tune and wails, then an elderly lady in a costume of tinsel and a top hat walks from the small stage and around the tables reciting poetry in French. Old Adel is behind the bar, at least I assume he's Adel, and before we leave, M asks if he can play here next week. Adel reaches below the counter, pulls a sheet full of scrawled notes out and places it on top of the bar. It is a more organised affair than it looks. They agree on a time and we walk back towards the Récollets, M feeling very pleased.

The next Sunday, Harry, Nadine, and a bunch of their friends come to watch him play. His music is quiet and delicate and can barely be heard over the weekend conversations, including those of Nadine and her friends. I want to ask them to shut up but don't want to make a scene and I don't want to look like M's guardian. He doesn't mind, strumming away, picking at the strings, playing arpeggios that allow the scraping of his touch and the gaps in between to tell their own stories. We stay all afternoon and into the evening. Nadine gets drunk and falls into M's lap asking, 'But why didn't you *sing*?' Harry and M talk guitars and bands and I flash back to how difficult it was for Adrien to get along with my friends; he would have been sitting here stiffly, trying to find the flow but eventually giving up and staring off into the distance, as I would with his friends. Harry orders pizza from next door and we eat it at a table outside before Harry leaves and M and I move to the bar to talk to Adel and arrange to play another gig.

134

As we're about to leave a guy comes in from the street and walks up to us. In a thick French accent he says he passed earlier and heard M playing, then had to run to work. But he loved what he heard, he says, it was *captivant*. Where are we from, how can he hear more of M's music, he is a musician too – well, an actor but he sings – can he take us out to lunch tomorrow?

⌒

Fifth: Valentin.

He is young – younger than both of us. He speaks with the air of an *aristo*, using big, beautiful words and gestural flounces, but it was clear that day we met at Chez Adel, from his beaten-up waiter's clothes and dirty shoes, that he was one of us. He lives in the rue de la Grange-aux-Belles just down from Chez Adel, and that night as we left the bar he invited us in for a *tisane*. He lived behind a tall blue *porte cochère* in a tiny studio that was like a glorified motel room. He explained it had been the concierge's office. Big enough for a bed, a giant spa bath, which he showed us proudly, and for some reason a cumbersome green leather Chesterfield couch. We sat on the Chesterfield, Valentin the floor, and talked for hours. He asked a thousand questions and told funny, wild stories, some far-fetched but we sensed they were true. M was fascinated by him, and grateful he spoke such good English. We left looking forward to our Monday lunch date at the Verre Volé, a place the local Parisians loved but I had only tried once and was afraid of the menu consisting of earthy traditional French food like entrails and oxtail and, of course, *andouillette*.

Valentin is already at the table when we arrive, with his Korean friend Charles, and has ordered a bottle of wine that makes M and me die that little death you have when you drink your first glass of something incredible, doomed to chase that feeling forevermore. It seems Valentin is wealthy because the high price is written in chalk on the rack and after an entrée of terrine and cornichons he orders a new bottle from another shelf, revelling in our enjoyment of his selections. The waiter knows him and gives us great service, despite the fact I'm sure they recognise me from that time I came here with Nadine and she complained about being sat in the back room.

Valentin is dressed more elegantly today, but casual, in a loose shirt, pants and shined shoes, and Charles looks more cool graphic designer but would look very at home in Valentin's chateau playing backgammon while dinner is prepared. Valentin is an actor – he had a small yet vital role in a Bertolucci film recently, and he manages a seedy all-night bar near Châtelet to pay his rent (and his mother's). The clientele there are hookers and drug dealers, he says – a lot of characters, the odd knife fight. Charles is a writer. He speaks with Valentin in French mostly but with us in English. He has published three books and has a theory that the thing to do is to write dozens of books fast and get them published to maximise the chances of one hitting the big time. He is currently completing his twelfth book and hoping to avoid conscription. He does Korean barbecue at his place on Friday nights, says Valentin. Last week he ate so much beef he couldn't sleep, thought he'd gone mad.

M and I try to calculate the bill as we go, but Valentin keeps ordering and ordering – you must try this, you must try that. I tell him the *andouillette* story and he orders it without a second thought, along with the *boudin noir* and some urchins. He makes us close our eyes as they arrive and feeds us small mouthfuls of each before allowing us to know what they are, with a sip of the perfect wine to go with each. The textures and flavours are stranger and more intense than anything I've had before, but they excite me. M feels the same, though he found the *andouillette* confronting in some way, like having gotten too close to something he didn't want to know about. Valentin is curious about the play and he would be perfect to read The Sly Cad so I ask and he says *bah oui* as if it had always been the case. I offer Charles a role too, but he says no, he'll watch and analyse. Drunk and full, in the late afternoon M says '*L'addition?*' to the waiter – and Charles suddenly starts stomping and screaming. Valentin has already paid – he won the paying game, that Valentin explains he learned in Korea. To pay is to win. M asks if they play poker and says he'll cook dinner for us all one night. Valentin and Charles look genuinely excited by this. They kiss us goodbye and Valentin crosses the canal, and as we walk home the same way as Charles, he tells us Valentin has no money at all, but spends his entire pay each week on the first day. Nothing to worry about, he says, Valentin always gets through.

⌒

Sixth: the Alice play reading is a hit.

I didn't want to rehearse before the day, so at 4 pm all 24 members of the cast arrive at the Récollets, a riffraff bunch of people I know, a few I don't, French and German and Colombian and Japanese and American and English. Once everyone's arrived in the *cour* I take them up to the first floor where I've printed out scripts and placed chips and beers and bottles of Badoit all down the long table. We do a single read-through. My only direction to everyone is to go *à fond* with their roles, stick to the words as much as possible, but exaggerate and invent. The only mistake is to be small. The reading is a riot, strange accents and character choices, even the bookseller's daughter's Alice is surreal and terrifying, in her vibrant purple dress. M and I have spent the morning making big pots of dhal, so after the reading we go upstairs and turn up the music loud while everyone crams in and feasts, it's a party, and by the time we go downstairs we're all a bit drunk and festive. I've hung my collages around the space and set up wine and food on the tables, which people help themselves to as they arrive. M has hooked up some music and made a pre-show playlist of kooky jazz to create the atmosphere. The American Writer is there, no Carl, Chantal and Paolo her assistant, Charles, Marie-France and Hakim, a few of Nadine's friends, and a bunch of people I don't know, who I assume are residents from the Récollets. It's a reading but the room is as electric as a theatre and I'm as excited as I once was about stepping onto the stage, only this time I get to introduce the play and sit back and see what it's like to watch words I've written hard into the page be brought to life.

It's wild. The cast give it everything they've got and more – bringing the words out and off the page with choices I couldn't have dreamed, playing off each other, making fun of each other, being naughty, ugly, loud, stupid, tragic but always sticking to the written words. It's flawed, raw, but it doesn't seem to matter. At the end there's applause and drunken whooping. Valentin pops champagne and M turns the music up and the party is alive. Nadine is dancing, the bookseller's daughter is laughing, Antoine from the marionette theatre is there, I forgot I invited him. He comes to shake my hand. *'C'était fou,'* he says, and I take his 'mad' as a compliment. *'Merci!'* He turns and heads towards the door. He hated it. The American Writer is on his way out too, but turns to say, 'I liked that. You should make it a full-length play.' During the reading I snuck glances at him as he listened with his head down, smiling occasionally to himself.

Harry high fives me and says Congrats! What the fuck was *that?* Charles found it challenging but there are some themes he'd like to discuss with me. Valentin loved it, he thought it was 'sexy'. Chantal liked it too, she says, though she couldn't understand a word. I profit from the moment to ask if M and I could stay on a bit longer after August. She says that won't be a problem and to come and see her to sign the forms. I will, however, need to have a new project, she says. Do I have something in mind? Yes, I tell her, panicking. I'm writing a book. I'm booked to do a reading at the English language bookshop.

'Super,' she says. 'And M?'

'He'll be launching his new album, performing shows in Paris.'

'Ça marche,' she says.

Seventh: we get jobs.

There is a missed call on my phone and when I play the message back I can't understand a word. Something about *conception-rédaction*, a *brochure*, an *agency*. It takes four goes to get down the number.

In second year, I'd had an idea that I could do some writing here, shine some light on the English I saw around town – shops selling *stranger wine, croque monsieur* translated as *crunch mister*, ads for burgers called VERY SWEET CHEESE. A restaurant called EAT ME. The Hotel Belter. A shop called HAND. (Have A Nice Day.) Warm cheese goat salad, my favourite vintage shop THANX GOD I'M A VIP. Fatty Mode the plus-sized dress shop, *Sneakers is the new black* (really?), *All you need is sneakers* (really?), Heartless Jeans, a BS company, *Be relax*, ASS CHICKEN, a band called NITS, an exhibition called *SHART*, Butt Fashion, a band called ROCK ON MY PUSSY. The list went on. The pinnacle was a billboard for a shoe company plastered all around the city, in which a model is helping a plastic mannequin version of herself try on a shoe, the slogan reading, *PLAY WITH FASHION. PLAY WITH YOURSELF.*

In Australia I had worked in an advertising agency part time to support myself through drama school, and they'd had me writing brochures for caravans and campaigns for teen fashion, chocolate and erectile dysfunction tablets. Copywriting work in France could be fun – and I could work with the agencies in French, explain in their language why *play with yourself* is a bad choice. Bet it was good money, and if I freelanced I would be able to work in my own time, so I could be available for auditions and acting gigs.

I sent messages on the contact forms of all the advertising agencies I could find on the internet. Months went by with no response. Then at a fancy party one night with Adrien, I got talking to a chick who worked for a big agency; she told me I'd never break in via the generic online forms but she had a contact list of all the creative directors in Paris. The next day she sent it through to me *STRICTEMENT CONFIDENTIEL*. I spent days composing the perfect email and creating the perfect image of myself in a curriculum vitae – it wasn't like they were going to call Australia. I got a few emails back – auto responses, dead addresses, a few '*merci*, we will keep you on file's and a few 'how did you get this address?'s. After that, nothing. School ended, my scholarship ran out, Nadine helped me get some work teaching Business English to bankers, and I got a few of my own students and did some translation work which was horribly paid, if at all.

And now, eighteen months later, a call. *Votre profil nous intéresse.*

M is sleeping so I tiptoe out into the hall and press redial. My heart is thumping; speaking French on phones is still a challenge. The man who answers speaks in a torrent and I focus on the essential – *brochure – papier – rencontre – demain?*

'*Oui*,' I say, imagining I'm Séverine and mimicking her physicality when she would talk to producers or clients on the phone: lips pouted, hip out, eyebrows slightly raised.

JAYNE-SÉVERINE:
Tomorrow morning at 10, *c'est parfait.*

The next day I put on the best clothes I have and some makeup and take the métro to the 5th, close to the Salpêtrière, trying not to think about it, and get off at a stop that means I don't have to pass the hospital walls. The agency smells just like the one back home – do all advertising agencies smell the same and are they all full of the same well-dressed women and men with bald heads and sneakers? Two hip bald guys interview me and say they liked my CV. They ask me to name my price to work on a brochure for a paper company. I'm floored, what am I worth? The amount they suggest is far more than what I was thinking, but I put my best Séverine face on and, after consideration, say okay. I have no idea how much work this involves, perhaps months, perhaps I'm being ripped off, but the amount makes the future feel solid – the first time I've looked ahead.

We celebrate that night by inviting Valentin and Charles over to play poker. My neck is sore. They show up with two bottles of fine champagne, some good dry *saucisson*, and their friend Fanny and her boyfriend Jean-Yves who is a huge dick, talking about *verlan* – commonly spoken street French in which words are broken in two and the syllables reversed – and how it must never be accepted by the Académie Française and how the Petit Robert should be ashamed of itself – it's not correct

French. We all argue, M says surely a dictionary should reflect the French that people actually speak. Fanny is as hilarious as her name and doesn't mind that I find it funny. She has a Russian accent when she speaks English. When I tell her this she says that's odd because her great-grandparents on one side were Russian. Valentin confirms there is not a trace of Russian accent in her French. It must be some kind of latent DNA thing. Fanny has a gap tooth like Betty Blue.

VALENTIN:
Cool scar.

FANNY:
What's it from?

JAYNE:
Accident de ski.

VALENTIN:
You land on the side of your face?

JAYNE:
Yeah.

FANNY:
Where, Méribel? Courchével? Where you ski?

JAYNE:
Euhh.

VALENTIN:
I broke my leg – my friend Stéph broke his back!
Mad shit. Can I see – closer? *Ouf* – you land on a rock?
Oh shit. What's really happen?

JAYNE:
You know those elevators that aren't protected?

I tell the story.

VALENTIN:
Holy fuckian shit.

We invite them all to come and watch a band with us on Friday night in an outdoor amphitheatre in Montmartre, some friends of M's from Melbourne. On Friday it's hot and I don't know what to wear. I settle on a too-short skirt and my brown boots, instantly regretting it as we take our seats on the curved stone steps, sure his friends can see right inside me. Valentin arrives with a girl he just met on the métro and Charles sits up the back with Fanny. The ambient lights of the city rise behind the stage, a few stars twinkle behind the thick city veil.

M squeezes my hand. His hair is still wet from the shower and he has sunglasses on and he is happy – his worlds are colliding in a fantastic way. I am happy too. It's a perfect night, the ambient sounds of Montmartre hover around us which we can just hear over the sound of the band. The lead singer is wearing board shorts and thongs like he's at a pool party in suburban Melbourne. They are so cool and ironic I wonder if they translate here and they seem to, the crowd is loving it, the music is so happy and weird your legs won't stay still. I stand up at one point and dance around a bit on our ledge, then get embarrassed and sit down again. M listens intently, his head moving gently to the beat.

After the show, the band and a big bunch of friends walk to the restaurant M booked on the rue Lepic. It's a noisy, bustling place: old worn tables, loud waiters, the rambunctious mob of us squeezed into the corner. M and I are sitting next to two English guys, friends of the band, one of them, Dorian, dressed like an old dandy, and one who reminds me of the Artful Dodger, accent and everything. I tell him this and he laughs, and even that sounds like the character.

'What happened to the Artful Dodger?' I wonder out loud. 'Not the actor, I mean what happened to the character in the story?'

Dorian says in his clipped accent that he believes the Artful Dodger was caught with a snuff box and in the novel it is alluded to that he is shipped off to Australia. We are all very drunk and it suddenly feels like we're on a ship too. We drink more. The Artful Dodger guy lives in Belleville and works at the horse races. He *is* the Artful Dodger. I put his number in my phone under Artfl Dodga.

It's 4 am by the time M and I stumble down through the messy streets back to the Récollets. M is slurring, he's a very cute drunk.

'That guy offered me a job,' he says.

'What guy?'

'I can't remember his name. Pom guy.'

'The one who looked like the Artful Dodger?'

'Oh yeah! I think so.'

'What's the job?'

'At the track. He works for a betting syndicate.'

'What does that mean?'

'Not sure. He goes out to the track to report back – stats, numbers, pool sizes, something. It's not much money, but it's cash.'

'Would you want to stay here for a job at a racetrack?'

'Maybe. And music perhaps. I didn't tell you, but I got some news the other day.'

'What news?'

'The bass guitarist and the drummer I was going to form the new band with are leaving New York.'

'Why didn't you tell me?'

'I don't know. It seemed like another reason to stay in Paris, and I wasn't sure if I should.'

'Paris is so funny.'

'Yeah. She loves us.'

'She's rewarding us.'

'She wants me to stay.'

'She does that, the little minx, then she gets you in a headlock.'

'I think I love her too.'

'The slut.'

'For so long I've been *pushing* to find something. And since we've been here all this stuff is just happening, flowing.'

'It *is* naturally happening. We should probably just let it.'

I tell him about the Récollets, how we can stay longer if we like. I hadn't been sure about telling him this either.

'Wow.'

A drunk guy stops us and asks for *du feu* but I tell him I don't smoke, and M says *moi non smoke either.*

'Let's talk about it in the morning,' M says, stumbling on a crack.

Early next morning, he rolls over and says, 'I think I'll take that job. I think I want to stay in Paris. Is that weird for you?'

My first instinct is joy. Then panic. Oh God, this wasn't the plan.

'No,' I say. 'Not weird at all. Well, a bit. It wasn't the plan.'

'If I left now,' he says, 'it'd just be to stick to the plan, not because I want to.'

'I don't want you to go,' I tell him. This is true. It's confusing. 'But I want us to keep the freedom feeling we have.'

'Me too, I've become addicted to that.'

'It's such a good feeling.'

'Perhaps we can recreate that, without the going.'

I laugh. 'Maybe.'

'We can test it anyway,' he says. 'I don't have to stay here with you at the Récollets. I can easily move to my mate's place or see if there's a room somewhere around here.'

'Yeah, or you could just stay here.'

He smiles. 'Let's just take it a day at a time. Be completely honest. We have nothing to lose – it's all an experiment. I trust you to tell me if it's too much and you need some space. You can trust I'll tell you too.'

A cool breeze blows through the window. The first since we arrived.

The Cooling

The leaves fall and the Parisians return, the streets fill with people on determined trajectories. M spends long days out at the track; Vincennes, Enghien, Longchamp, Auteuil. His job is a simple task involving sending the pool sizes back to the office on a device called a PDA. He has to be sharp and quick with numbers in French, but other than that he has time to dream and listen to his music while learning all about the horses and jockeys, with a few flutters using the tips the Dodger sends him. In the evenings he returns to the Récollets, face flushed, asking questions about words and turns of phrases – 'Are they calling them DOGS (*chiens*) or SHITTY (*chiant*) – as in *ALLER CHIEN* or is it *ALLEZ, CHIANT!* (as in, GO YOU SHIT) or are they saying something else?' – and relating stories of the different courses and their moods – the champagne events with strawberries and cream, the crusty beer dens full of shouting old men and tickets piled on the floor like trodden snow. His eyes dance as he describes the characters he comes across, the skinny man and his fat wife wrapped in furs despite the raging heat, mirror man, who spends all day watching his old, worn self in the mirror rather than the race.

I stay in the Récollets and write. The chapters of the book are slowly forming and I tinker on them until my neck seizes up, playing with tense and tone and person. I'd rather be working on the play but am not sure what to do with it. I sent the script and synopsis to theatres in London and New York, and a few letters have come back, and a few email rejections. They like the writing, they say, but *can't take it on as a project at this time.*

It occurs to me that when writing the play I never thought about how it might actually be staged; I paid no attention whatsoever to the mechanics of it, creating dozens of settings with no cohesion, impossibilities like characters eating each other, flying, emerging from inside each other, being split in two with an axe. Twenty-four characters, with all their physical defects and costumes, not to mention the bizarre and complex sets … Anything is achievable in the theatre, but I was too lazy to think of that side of it and didn't want to hamper my imagination with practicalities.

Now I think of it, to stage *Alice Eat the Night Violet* would cost a fortune. The theatres must have been exhausted just reading it. Far cleverer to write a two-hander set in a dirt mound.

So, I've put the play to the side. It makes me sad. It doesn't want to be contained in a drawer. Just because it has no place in the practical realm, doesn't mean it's not alive. One day I'll figure it out. For now, I'll keep working on the book. For that I don't need any staging, anyone.

And there's the copywriting.

My inbox floods with requests, as other agencies learn I'm available and fast. I work diligently, beating deadlines and surprising them with my responsiveness, though the internet is terrible in the Récollets and my neck so rigid from the hard bed and typing I have reverted to wearing the wool scarf. My neck is annoying, but I'm managing to keep it to myself. The pain is so so boring, I once answered honestly when somebody asked me, and it brought down the mood so much I swore to myself never again. M worries when I tell him anything about it. It's best to just go with it, keep it to myself. Flashbacks and panic attacks too. These constant visions of ridiculous, even preposterous accidents playing out before my eyes. Baby thrown from bike seat into slow-moving garbage truck. Old man impaled on fence post of *jardin public*. Foot severed by motorbike. In every scenario it is somehow my fault. That makes the terror worse and I have to go back to the room, climb upstairs, get in bed and pull the pillow over my head.

One morning we're at L'Atmosphère, hungover. It's 11:25 and the women behind the bar are refusing to let us sit outside to drink a coffee because at 11:30 they make up the tables for lunch. Paris is exasperating with its regimented hours for breakfast, lunch, *goûter, apéro,* dinner, but we're trying not to grump as we walk down the canal towards Prune, where they at least allow us to sit at the bar. Fuck those sluts. We're sledging them in an upbeat way when a strange noise behind us makes us stop and turn around, and before I can register what's going on, M has leapt into the middle of the street and is waving his arms frantically above his head.

'Stop! STOOOOP!'

I look back up the canal. Near the crossing outside L'Atmosphère is a flurry of colour and noise and now M is sprinting up the road. Two African women in vibrant traditional robes are shouting and wailing, a truck has stopped on the crossing and a burly man has jumped down from the cab, hurling abuse in a deep voice. My heart thumps, M is pulling something from beneath the truck – a baby stroller, on its side – oh god, there's a baby in there – I get the baby out – he's okay, shhh shhh, but he's silent – why isn't he crying? – now he's screaming thank god thank god – M is under the truck now – an older boy of about five springs out from behind the wheel – He is bleeding, his hand! M has him – I have the baby – oh god – a woman screaming – *LE CAMION BON DIEU OH DIEU OH DIEU* – both women are hysterical – the truck driver is yelling at them it's their fault, their fault – M is talking to the little boy as he pulls off his own jumper and wraps the boy's hand in it, M is trying to speak French, *je ne parle pas bien Français,* he is smiling at the boy, saying to him *do you think I speak good French, I am terrible aren't I, what is your name?* His name is Léo, he tries to look at his hand but M keeps distracting him, saying funny things, speaking so calmly, I am cradling the baby, I take him across to the curb to have a proper look at him – oh god I should not have moved him. One of the African women approaches – I can't let go – *merci merci madame* she says – I let go, the lady is calming him now, rocking the baby and patting his back – *shhhhh – il est okay, ça va, ça va, il est okay ...*

That is all the children from beneath the truck. They are okay. Everything is okay. It was a big fright, but everything is fine, the boy's hand has a small cut, that is all. But I see blood, the road flooded with it, the boy's arm severed, the baby's skull flattened by the wheel, it's fine, it's fine, it's okay, it's nothing. They are okay, it's a cut. A crowd has gathered, an ambulance arrives, the police, the other woman is in shock, ranting and shaking her hands, the truck driver has stopped railing and is now walking in circles, rubbing his forehead. People are murmuring *les nounous, les nounous,* they assume they're the nannies to the little white boys but I hear one of the ladies telling the policeman they're her nephews, *je suis la tante,* it's the boys' aunties, fucking racists. M stays by the little boy's side as the *pompiers* check him over. The auntie has now calmed slightly. The baby is fine, *shhh,* he's fine. The little boy waves to M as the ladies walk him away, giving M a deep nod of gratitude. Then they're gone.

M and I stand for a moment in silence then sit down on the gutter. I put my head over my knees. The truck driver is being questioned, he is calm now, sorrowful. M explains to me what happened: the truck driver had been sitting at a red light when the women began to walk across. They were short, and the truck was close to the crossing – M guesses that from his position in the cab the driver couldn't see them, and when the lights changed he began to roll forward, almost crushing them. One fraction more of the wheel roll ...

'They're okay,' says M, sensing my shock. 'They're fine.'

'You saved their lives.'

People pass by us and rub M on the back, saying '*Bravo, merci, courageux,* the children were lucky.' The police come to question us and M relays what he saw, I translate. They take our names and addresses. The police seem to have the impression that the 'nannies' stepped out when their crossing light was red. They weren't NANNIES. They were

TANTES, I say. They tell me to calm myself down. I tell them the truck driver must have started rolling when his light was still red. Otherwise why would the women have been on the road with the children?

The crowd has dispersed, the truck is gone, the only trace it happened is a tiny splash of the boy's blood on the pavement. The two women from L'Atmosphère ask us to come back with them for coffee but we say *non merci*, grateful now they had refused us, or those boys may not have been so lucky.

'Let's go and get something warm,' says M, taking my hand and we walk together back down the canal as before, which feels bizarre, like we've just had a bad dream. The colours are too bright, the sounds too loud. All I can see around me is accidents, crushed skulls, mangled bodies, buildings falling, pot plants crashing down from great heights. Perhaps M is feeling the same way, I'm too scared to ask in case he thinks I'm mad. We continue past Prune to La Marine, who are in full lunch mode now, but they don't mind us having a cup of tea. Valentin and Charles are at a corner table with friends, I hope they haven't spotted us. I order a pot of earl grey for the two of us, which we sit and stare at for a moment before M pours the hot liquid into two white cups.

'*Coucou* lovers,' says Valentin, leaning over the table. Charles stands smiling behind him.

'Hey,' M says. 'We can't talk. We've had a trauma.'

Valentin pulls up a chair and sits down, Charles too. They want to know what happened, and it feels good to hear M say it out loud. He is shocked, but able to recount it accurately and with humour, like – you won't believe what happened. Just one of those freak things. When he finishes the story Valentin says nothing, then orders two whiskeys neat, which we drink obediently like medicine. It helps. He orders another round for us and the two of them leave us and pay our bill before we know it. Nausea sets in. M suggests we walk, so we head to République and into the Square du Temple, lying in a brief patch of sunshine before returning to our room to lie together holding hands until the sun goes down.

He asks if I'm okay and I tell him I'm fine.

'You don't seem okay.'

'Are *you* okay?'

'I'm okay. Still a bit shocked. But I'm just so relieved they're fine.'

They're fine. They're fine they're fine they're fine.

'Has your body slowed down now?' I ask him.

'Slowed down?'

'Like, is your heart beating fast?'

'No.'

He rolls towards me. I cross my arms tightly across my body.

'I'm just shocked that the police officer would assume it was the women's fault,' I say.

'But it is possible that they walked out on the red man,' he says, 'we do it all the time on that intersection. They might have assumed the guy saw them and would let them —'

'WHO WOULD DO SOMETHING LIKE THAT?' I blurt. 'Sorry. It's just – who on this planet would ever step out in front of a truck *with children?* They assumed they were safe!'

'You're right, you're right.'

'It is impossible that they were responsible. It makes no human sense.'

'I agree. I agree.'

I want to make him angry at me. I want to make him leave. But everything I throw at him he responds to calmly, with understanding. I am annoyed at my weakness, resentful, annoyed that I might need him, even a bit.

He sleeps with his arm around me. In the morning I walk down to Chez Prune, noticing the tiny blood stain at the crossing. I'm relieved to see the stain, it confirms that it happened. Again I feel bad for being relieved at something terrible. I sit down and drink a coffee at an indoor table where it's warm. M joins me later. He is in a good mood. We talk about other things.

⁓

A surprise call from Antoine, the director of the marionette theatre, as I'm standing in the queue at the Franprix. He actually loved the play. He's wondering if he could workshop it with the students at the marionette school attached to the theatre, with a view to developing it into a full production next year.

I step aside in the queue, rubbing my neck which is tight as a rock. I can't believe it. I had never thought of that. I tell him, yes yes yes, of course and we arrange to meet and I hang up in a spin.

A *marionnette* show. Of course! I had never been able to see the play on stage because I'd been envisaging it with live actors. It is not a play for live actors. It's a play for *marionnettistes!* Just a handful – four or five – could do all the characters. So much more room for madness and play and the impossible.

Full production.

My mind goes wild imagining the puppets they'll use, the devices, the shadows and objects and sound. I pay for the milk and batteries and toilet paper and rush up the Faubourg-Saint-Denis to tell M, who is thrilled and asks me what *marionnettes* exactly are.

His album has come back from the Master. We turn off the lights and listen and I try to hear the puff of air but can't, though the whole thing sounds beautiful, even without Bakehouse Blues.

He has received the artwork from a guy in Norwich that he commissioned after seeing his drawings in a poetry anthology, in particular an image of a bunny in a bucket, that was sweet and funny and a bit dark. The artwork the guy has sent in response to M's brief which was *anything you come up with in response to the music* – is equally strange and bewildering: owls and cats and stacks of books, a tin soldier on a horse, a woman holding a baby in the lamplight. At nights, M has been playing with the designs and starting to put a band together for the launch, which Franck has helped him book for November at a good-sized venue, La Scène Bastille, a place I used to go with Adrien.

His ad on Craigslist yields a tall, bald Texan bass guitarist and a short, feisty French-Canadian drummer, but he can't find a lead guitarist who doesn't want to pull bendy notes or cock-rock strums. It doesn't matter for now he says, and asks if I might like to play some of the guitar lines on keyboard to fill it out a bit. Really? I haven't played anything since bad clarinet in the high school band. All I have to do is play the parts M has already written for the songs, he tells me, so I get a texta and mark the keys to push. M likes me in the band and I like being part of it and we trundle together a few nights a week out the Récollets and down the rue du Faubourg-Saint-Denis with his guitar and Harry's amp and a lumpy bag of percussion instruments on a silver trolley he's bought from the Festi Bazaar, to the sticky carpets of the Studio Bleu on the rue des Petites-Écuries, collecting two sixpacks of Tsingtao from the Asian grocer on the way. Annick takes the feeling of the songs and paints with her drum kit, Dan strums the bass in his dry Texan way, and his dry, laconic sense of humour makes us all laugh. The songs come to life and we drink afterwards at Jeannette like we've known each other forever.

One night at Jeannette the Dodger is there with a friend from Canada and invites us to play *boules* the next day with them. My neck is so bad the next day from sleeping wrong on the hard bed I almost make an excuse but don't want to be boring, so we walk up the canal in the crisp late afternoon, the weather helping me justify my burying into the scarf. It's perfect autumn, the air clear and cold, the trees half-bare: Paris seasons seem to obey the rules as much as Parisians do mealtimes. The Dodger is outside the Bar Ourq with tall blond Cam. Cam is serious about sports, The Dodger says, by manner of introduction. He invited us as he considered us serious sportspeople: this was not to be taken as some fun, gleeful Sunday outing. M laughs. Cam has his own monogrammed boules set, which saves us having to borrow the grimy ones from the bar.

Cam throws the little white ball along the gravel.

'Got your technique sorted?' he asks M, flexing his fingers.

'Errr, no,' says M, laughing and sipping his beer.

'Ladies first,' says Cam.

'Lady?' I say. 'I don't see a lady.'

My technique is the same one that would drive Dad nuts when we played carpet bowls – ignore the dot on the side of the ball and shoot right over it, straight and clunky rather than with the elegant, weighted swing.

'Up the guts!' I shout as I launch the ball along the ground.

Ow. Something has happened to my neck. Shellshock. It takes a few moments to remember where I am. The boys' eyes follow the silver ball that moves sloppily along the gravel, stopping way short, but straight in line with the kitty.

'Terrible!' calls The Dodger. His voice is dimmed, like someone turned the volume down. My eyes are blurred, the back of my tongue has gone numb. I look down at my fingers – they move. Take a step – fine. My neck feels like it's swelling inside, a splintering feeling. I watch the Dodger as he steps up to take his place. Someone has painted my eyeballs with pale blue gel.

'Rip 'n roll!' calls The Dodger.

He backspins his *boule* in a crazy motion up in the air and it lands heavily on the gravel, sending stones in the air. I move to the side and sit down on a bench, ensuring my body reads *watching* and doesn't draw attention.

'I like it!' says M.

If I stay looking forward it'll be okay. M swings his arm back and neatly guides the *boule* in an elegant right curve around to nestle to the right of the kitty, the closest so far. Whoops and cheers.

'Classic!' says The Dodger.

Cam lines up his *boule*.

'Hit and miss!'

He fangs his ball as hard as he can towards M's, knocking it slightly towards the kitty.

'Hit!' says Dodger.

'Oh no!' says M.

This is the best game ever. God, don't let them know about my neck. Don't let me ruin the moment. My sight is still blurred but I can make out the balls and what's going on enough to keep playing, keeping my action small and underarm, making it my style, keeping my neck rigid at all costs. *Turn your head, fall down dead.*

We play until the lights come on along the canal and the smaller boats have all come in for the night, leaving just the ferry going across and back between the two cinemas. The *quai* is crowded with drinkers and picnickers, puffing steam into the cool night sky.

'Loser buys dinner!' says Dodge. Oh no. What excuse can I make? There is no excuse to be made. Better to die at dinner than go home and kill the party.

It somehow happens to be Cam, which M and I are silently grateful for because if it was us, we'd be eating burgers called VERY SWEET CHEESE from the Quick. My vision is still blurry and my neck throbbing but I'm not dead and am still functioning.

Cam chooses the Bistrot des Oies, near the apartment he's staying in on the rue Marie-et-Louise, and he insists on ordering. He selects the Frenchest things on the very French menu, because, he tells us, he's leaving tomorrow and wants to make himself sick so he won't miss the food. The rich food and intense smells make me nauseous but I manage to eat enough to keep the attention off me, making an excuse about having had a huge lunch. M squeezes my knee under the table. I keep my focus forward.

As I lie stiff as a board in bed that night, M rolls towards me. 'Is everything okay?'

'Yes, why?'

'You seem distant.'

'Oh no, I'm fine.'

But the next morning my neck is tight as a rock and pain is shooting down my legs and back up through the top of my head like a fountain. M goes to work, thankfully, and Bérénice says to come straight away. She makes me lie down on my back this time, places her hands on my shoulders then moves them towards my neck. I wince and she tells me to relax but my body has gone into a state of panic. *Detendez-vous, detendez-vous.*

'I'm worried I've broken it again,' I tell her. 'Or splintered a bit off into my brain, behind my eyes.'

'You have to let me touch you,' says Bérénice.

Tears spill down my cheeks. I am terrified. She reassures me that she's not going to hurt me but that she needs to check me. My muscles have seized up, she tells me, and until they are loosened we will not know what is wrong.

I let her move her fingers and thumbs lightly up to the base of my neck where the fracture was. *Shhhh.* She presses lightly into the muscles of my lower neck, they spasm and clench, *you must <u>relax</u>* she barks at me and I try, I do, but I can't help feeling that with the pressure of her touch I am going to die. I am not thinking this, my body is. She moves her hands up to my head and presses down into the back of my skull. It feels like a cavern, open like a cup, like in a cartoon where they're eating the brains out. It is so tender my eyes feel like they are going to pop right out of my skull.

'*C'est bien, c'est bien, laissez aller, laissez aller.*'

I start to cry. It's like she's burst a dam.

'*Oui, oui, c'est ça c'est ça.*' You have been holding on very tight and now your neck has reminded you that you need to relax, to take care of your neck, to let go of the emotions.

The fracture has knitted, she assures me, I am safe. I must get it out of my head that there is still a break there. She massages the delicate muscles on my neck and head as a new torrent escapes me. Ugly, unrecognisable sound, from some deep, ancient swamp, guttural, vile, she keeps massaging insistently, pushing it out. *Laissez aller …*

I cry and cry and she rubs and rubs and afterwards I feel empty and embarrassed and also a bit lighter.

Though the break is healed, she tells me, my neck will always be fragile. She adds, upbeat, that I will probably always feel the approach of rain, like old people! If I don't take constant care of it, the tension will build and damage like this will happen, or worse, torn muscles, neurological problems, spasming, even spine damage. I am okay, my neck had just become blocked and the throwing of the *boule* triggered a muscular reaction, inflammation and possibly a small tear. She prescribes a host of medications.

I'm to come back in a week, she tells me. I must not miss the appointment.

At home M is quiet, I can sense he feels like he's done something wrong.

'There's something embarrassing I need to tell you,' I say, and tell him about the neck. It's so dumb and hard to explain. 'I haven't been giving you the cold shoulder. I just literally couldn't turn to you. My neck has just been stuck. Even kissing has hurt.' It's amazing how much affection is expressed through the neck.

'You funny thing. Let me kiss you.' He comes and moves his face to kiss me without me having to move mine. 'Let's go and get a proper mattress.'

'We can't afford one.'

'Let's find one anyway. We'll figure it out.'

We don't end up needing the mattress.

The next night M tells me to meet him outside the Châtelet métro in the Place Sainte-Opportune. He emerges from the métro entrance, kisses me and leads me to the *bistrot* opposite. I'm surprised, but allow myself to be led. We haven't voluntarily eaten in a restaurant in a while because I have run out of money – though the copywriting work is well-paid I won't see any cash for at least a few weeks. M's track money is cash but not much, and the rent on the Récollets is overdue.

The waiter takes our coats and seats us in a cosy booth.

'What is it? Is everything okay?'

M replies by ordering a bottle of champagne. I stare at him in awe.

'How much did you win?'

'Enough for the rent and champagne and more.'

I sit back. 'No.' His cheeks gleam.

'And there's more.'

'More?'

To set up a betting account in France, he tells me, you have to have an address here. So the betting syndicate rents a stack of the shittiest apartments in Paris, basically using them as letterboxes. The Dodger lives in the best one they've got, in the 19th – it's actually not that shitty apparently, and The Dodger pays no rent. No. Rent. He's been there a few months; before that he had been somewhere else slightly shittier. The apartment is in the rue des Annelets, just beside these old music studios called Plus XXX, where Serge Gainsbourg used to do a lot of his recording. Anyway, they needed another place closer to the office in Opéra, so The Dodger is moving in there, which means this one will be sitting there empty. Do I see where he is headed …

'Are you *serious*?' I ask. 'For no rent?'

'For zero rent.'

'That is not possible.'

'Oh, but it is.'

'That is so cool! You'll love it there.'

A soft look comes across his face. 'I thought you might move up there with me?'

'Oh no no. It's for you. I'll get my own joint.'

'If you like. But you won't be paid for weeks. This way we can live rent free until we at least get on our feet.'

'But that would be *living together*.'

'Well we are now, basically, aren't we?'

'No, this is just a hiatus like we agreed. Art camp. An extended art camp.'

'Sure,' he says without any display of disappointment or frustration. 'Well, the offer's there.'

We clink glasses. The bubbles light my soul. I know he's right. What's my plan going forward? I can't afford the Récollets on my own. Move in with Nadine? With Harry? The copywriting work has 60–90 day terms. How are people supposed to live? Perhaps they'll give me an advance.

And the thing is, free rent aside, I *want* to keep staying with him. I don't want to say 'living'. Just staying. It's fun. It's easy. I can't wait to get back to him each day and ask what he's done and tell him what I've done.

It feels natural. How stupid would it be not to move in there with him, just because I don't want things to progress any further.

'One last thing and I'll shut up,' he says. 'We are on the same page. This is a *free apartment in Paris*. When does anything like that ever come along in your lifetime? We would be taking advantage of that, just staying in there together – you living your life, me living mine. It doesn't have to mean a single thing. It's the outside world that says things like these have to mean things. We know it doesn't, yes? And then we get to live in the place and have our friends over and make it nice and live in the neighbourhood and live something different to your life in the 10th and your life in the 20th. A whole new thing. And that is all I will say.'

I pour the last of the bubbles into both our glasses.

'Let's go up and see it.'

M settles the bill and we get on our bikes and ride up through Belleville and into a very old Paris street with cracked pavements and old worn buildings, one painted pink with shutters that looks like it's been transported from the countryside. Number 33 is a basic beige brick building with balcony ledges that have pot plants hooked questionably over them. The door is dark red. We dump our bikes, punch in the code and head upstairs to the fourth floor where The Dodger is waiting for us.

'Welcome to your palace!'

I don't want to offend The Dodger but it's a scungy shithole.

'It's a scungy shithole!'

'It really is!' he says.

He pours champagne into three greasy cups and we clink them together, not bothering to tell him we've already drunk a bottle.

'It's a scungy shithole but trust me you'll love it. The Buttes right there, these shitty little old streets, the PMU on the rue de la Villette, the shops on Pyrénées.'

'M can give it a woman's touch,' I say, snooping around.

'You can give it anything the fuck you want. You can paint it, gut it, but don't put too much effort into it because things can always change in two seconds with these guys.'

He is talking like I'm coming too, which of course I am. We check out the scummy bathroom and the tiny bedroom with a sloping roof. The bed is lumpy. There are two windows that look out over the demolition site next door and the pollution-stained backs of a row of rambling old buildings, all pipes and drains and peeling paintwork. Then we sit at the wonky kitchen bar in the shabby little salon and drink the rest of the bubbles.

I love it, scungy shithole though it is. You could take up the terrible lino or put rugs down over it. There is a washing machine: no more scrounging for tokens for the clothes-destroying communal washers in the Récollets.

'Thanks Dodger,' says M.

'Thank the dodgy world of gambling.'

'Do you eat in here?' I ask.

The Dodger laughs, looking at the grimy shelves, the cracked walls. 'When you live here you don't *have* to.'

All the things you could do if you didn't have to pay rent. Travel, save, buy clothes from boutiques in the Marais, eat whatever you want off the menu at La Marine. It would be fun to live in a new *quartier*, get to know your neighbours, actually live in a home with an address, pay the *assurances*. It's close to the 20th here, the rue de la Chine only a ten-minute walk up the rue de Belleville, but it feels unfamiliar. Métro Jourdain, line 11. I haven't taken the line 11 much, it's a peculiar line, brown on the map, with only a few stops on it cutting north-east to central, never crossing to the left bank. There's a secret feeling up here, the Paris Haussmann forgot. Serge in his hideaway, Édith Piaf singing in bars.

'Let's go to dinner,' says The Dodger. He leads us up the rue des Annelets and down a pretty, run-down street to a dodgy-looking *bistrot* on the rue des Pyrénées, where everyone's eating the same thing. I ask the Dodger what it is, but he doesn't know.

'Some kind of steak? I always get the same thing, *poulet basquaise*, but let's get what they're having.'

We order and when it comes it's drenched in gravy and served with *pommes-frites*. We tuck in and our eyes meet – it tastes like steak but there is something mealy about it, powdery almost. I call the waiter and ask what in fact it is. '*Foie,*' he says. I'm glad we didn't ask first because I would never have ordered it, and I'm glad to have tasted it like the *andouillette* but I hate it, it's too rich. I move on to the chips as The Dodger munches his down. M is unsure too, leaving it to the side.

'Perhaps it will grow on me,' he says.

After dinner we walk to a dark little bar called La Cagnotte on a corner closer up to our place, just opposite the Monoprix and a wide *primeurs*. The Dodger's favourite drink is a *kir à la chataigne*, a chestnut liqueur with cheap wine, and it's instantly ours too. The Dodger smokes and I want to smoke one too but don't. M doesn't think it's sexy, not that that would stop me. Well, perhaps a bit.

There's a bizarre, colourful flyer for a circus on the bar with a picture of a creepy clown on it that reads *VIVE LE CIRQUE* and I pick it up and turn to M.

'Our first home decoration.'

He gives me a wide smile.

Dodger waves us goodbye later from his balcony.

'See you soon, homemakers!'

M holds my hand as we walk in the feathering rain down towards the Buttes Chaumont.

Annelets

We move to the rue des Annelets a few days later, hauling our stuff over in taxis from the Gare de l'Est. Harry helps. The apartment feels even grottier without The Dodger's stuff in it, so M and I go straight to the Monoprix and bring back mops and scourers and buckets, hiding the piles of disgusting crockery and kitchenware behind curtains and in boxes, unsure if we're allowed to throw them out. The walls won't stop being yellowed from decades of smoke, but we manage to get some of the smell out of the floors, and by the time night falls the place feels liveable.

In the bedroom, beneath a pile of junk Harry threw on the bed in the move, we discover a brand-new mattress and pillows.

'Did you do that?' I ask M.

'No.'

'Then who?'

'Bet I know.'

Dodge. My situation has obviously been discussed, despite my attempts to hide it, but rather than feel betrayed, a sense of brotherly warmth wraps itself around me.

We take off the plastic and lie on the mattress in the moonlight. It is supportive in all the right places, which makes me want to cry. We look out at the rear of the buildings opposite, the heating vents and chimneys, people's back stairs and bathroom windows. It's ugly in such a beautiful way. It feels like ours. Something new – nothing to do with my history in Paris.

The apartment remains defiantly scungy but we quickly adapt and make it a home, M's guitars and leads through the living room, my laptop in the little cubicle near the front window. We have no pot plants. The street below feels like something from the old film *The Red Balloon*. M waves to me from down there on his way to the track, his old man hat on, his black satchel with his notebooks and reading books in it. He writes a journal every day, I'm dying to read it. What is his experience of all this? Is he happy?

He seems to be. He has such an even temperament that it can be hard to tell. He says he wakes in the morning feeling so happy about the idea of coffee he could explode with joy. Despite my sensitivity he still comes towards me, he has no fear of rejection and is never upset if I'm in one of my phases where I can't be touched. His life in Paris is full, of work, friends, music. Every night he's excited about dinner – he cooks or we go to the Bariolé (we grow to love the *foie*) or the Indian restaurant on the rue du Jourdain. A couple of Australians in there on their honeymoon strike up a conversation with us one night, saying Paris was nice but Australia was better and they couldn't wait to get home. We realised how far we felt from Australia in that moment. M squeezed my hand on the way home and said let's never go back.

⌒

Nadine brings my stuff over and helps me arrange it, including a bag of clothes she doesn't wear anymore. She thinks the flat is great and can't believe we're getting it for free. She and Didier have been looking for an apartment together but they're all either too expensive or too far away. She refuses to compromise.

'And you wouldn't just move to his place in the 6th?' I ask, hanging dresses from the pile on the bed.

'No way,' she says, picking a pair of M's undies up from the bed and throwing them on the floor, before lying back on the bed with a box of macarons. 'It needs to be somewhere we can stay. I want some *roots*. I want a kitchen. I want to get married and have some babies.'

'Why?'

'What do you mean why?'

'Why would you want to do that?'

'You want that.'

'No, I don't.'

'You did want that. With Adrien.'

I don't know that I did want that with Adrien, though I said yes to his proposal. Looking back I suspect I just wanted the thrill. It was sexy to be asked, and sexy to play the role. But when it came to the reality of it, the whole thing crumbled.

'You and M are getting married,' she says.

'No we are not. We're friends. Sex friends. But friends.'

'You marry your best friend,' she says. 'Or you should. That's what my mum says.'

'I'll marry you then.'

'Ha.'

'My mum and dad were best friends.'

'Mine weren't. Didier is a good friend. He's not my best friend.'

'Will you marry Didier?'

'In a heartbeat.'

'M is a very good friend.'

'My friend too.'

'He is,' I say. 'He thinks you're hilarious.'

'What do you mean?'

'He thinks you're funny.'

She is offended by this.

'As in, he thinks you're lovely.'

Always minefields with Nadine, I can never get it right.

'I thought you wanted me to marry Adrien?' I say, changing the subject.

'I did want you to marry Adrien. I love Adrien.'

'Then why do you want me to marry M?'

'I didn't say I *want* you to marry M. I said M is the one you marry.'

'How do you know you'll love someone forever?'

'You don't. That's why it's so romantic.'

'It's suicide. Love suicide. You have something great, so you murder it with paperwork.'

'I don't see it like that.'

'Sorry, I'm just being devil's advocate. I like the idea of *proposing*. That's romantic. But I don't know if I'd want the actual marriage.'

'Then just keep proposing to people.'

'I like being bridesmaid. Can I be your bridesmaid, Nadine?'

I always thought love was wild – it should take you by the throat. You should want to disappear into the other person, your heart should hurt, you should feel out of control. You should obsess over your lover night and day, not be able to sleep, desire only to see them and nothing else. You should ride your bike across Paris for them, in the wee hours of the morning, scratch and claw at them so as to make them even more a part of you. They should tantalise you, tease you, fight with you because your actions touch them so deeply, and their actions touch you so deeply you feel you're bleeding inside. It is beyond explanation, what you have, incomprehensible to anyone else. Private. Beyond language, beyond cultures, you share a language only the two of you speak. That is love. That is the one.

'That is the one you fuck and murder,' says Nadine, licking her fingers. 'M is the one you marry.'

'You make it sound so un-hot.'

'It is hot. Kindness is hot. Sanity is hot.'

'But how do you keep it hot?'

'It gets hotter with age rather than burning out like a comet.'

'How do you know so much about it?'

'Oh you know. I read.'

'Do you feel that with Didier?'

'I do actually. We are not a comet.'

'Are you cosy then? Like two old people?'

'You make it seem like there's two options – comet or resignation. You can have the in-between you know.'

'You're right, that is how I see it.' I still can't believe every day that life with M can be simple and easy and yet not boring. I keep waiting for it to burst into flames or die a slow, banal death.

'It might blow up or die out,' she says. 'But it may not.'

'I suppose we'll both see.'

Nadine takes a last bite of macaron, pushes the pastel green box to the side and says she has to go. In the box she has left a dozen perfect semi-circles in an array of pastels, each with its signature front-teeth mark.

Antoine's face looks like the carved wood of the *marionnettes à gaine* in his theatre, though they have no face, just a nose, until they're dressed up, made-up, hair and features added. Everyone looks like a *marionnette* after you've looked at one. On the day I did the audition, a lifetime ago it feels, he had us work with all kinds of puppets and dolls and objects. The most important thing was finding the truth of what the character needed to do and finding the articulation around that. It was incredibly hard, my entire being felt used up by the end of the day as I battled between servitude to the object and direction of it. It felt as much a technical art as exposingly human, and as we watched each other work, like at Lecoq when Marie-France was *juste*, some performers simply melded with their *marionnette* and a sort of magic took place, a fusion of life and the innocence of death, more moving and mesmerising than anything I'd seen.

Do I want to perform in the show? Antoine asks, sipping his *chocolat chaud*. What kind of middle-aged man drinks *chocolat*? Antoine's hand hair is grey and runs all the way to his knuckles. It was him that suggested we meet in the Marais, he had a meeting there, thank goodness, so I didn't need to make an excuse about going to see him at the theatre. An irrational and embarrassing fear of the 20th only seems to have kept building since the time I saw his show, something impossible to understand, and when I try to, I go into a state of panic. I simply don't go there and don't think about it. It's inconvenient that the theatre is there, but it's helped make things clear in my head about the play. I will be the writer, but nothing else. Leave the script with Antoine, let the company do what they will with it, without me getting in the way.

No, I tell him, and explain my physical situation, and that I'm most interested in leaving the script in their hands and seeing what they come up with. I won't interfere at all in the process, just let it unfold and come to see it at the end. He is happy with the plan, but he will need the script in French. This throws me. The script has virtually no resemblance to the text from the French graphic novel and yet, how to adapt these nonsensical words? Antoine says nobody in their theatre speaks English and I wouldn't want to give the script to a translator, they wouldn't understand.

Do you know anyone?

Marie-France. Of course.

We shake hands and I call Marie-France straight away. She is thrilled and says she will apply for funding on top of the fee Antoine has promised. It will also be the *cachet* she needs to keep her status as *intermittent du spectacle*, the system that keeps French artists fed. She barely understands English at all, but saw the reading and knows intrinsically the things I mean, and I can explain the words and details to her in French. Or, even better, I could leave her alone and see what she makes of it.

I can almost feel the play bursting out of the drawer.

⌒

The weather gets cold. M and I collect furniture from the street and *vide-greniers*, the local one in the bleak Place des Fêtes, yielding three old but pretty café chairs, a plastic children's table we use as a coffee table, a white tablecloth I bleach and throw over the plastic table, and a variety of chipped glassware and crockery. Our greatest investment is in the STOP, the rubber plunger that sucks the funk from the endlessly clogged drains. I feel guilty for my long hair as M heaves swamplands from the shower, but he doesn't seem to mind, just plonks them in the sink causing me to pretend-vomit.

In the mornings before the track, M rides down the canal to a Brutalist building near La Villette to French class, coming home with great stories. When working on *j'aime* and *je n'aime pas*, the teacher asked around the room what people like and don't like. Most said something like *I don't like vegetables, I like coffee*, and one quiet Japanese girl said *je n'aime pas SATAN*. M wanted to say 'I like my sweetheart', but instead of saying *j'aime ma chérie*, he said to the teacher, *je t'aime ma chérie*. 'I love you my darling.' The teacher blushed and told him what he'd said, which made him laugh and blush too. The fact that he wanted to say he liked me makes me blush too, when he tells me the story.

His language is growing, in unexpected ways – rather than fussing over grammar and verb tables he's more interested in learning from the streets and repeating what he hears. On the way home from class he began stopping at a street basketball court to watch the habitual group of towering young guys that have owned the court for years twist and scramble and shoot. At first he would watch, noting their moves and listening to their language he couldn't understand – French, but with the words all mixed up. After a few days he gathered the courage to step onto the side of the court, where at first he was ignored or stared down but eventually, as a joke, invited to play, where he shot hoops and proved he was able. When he went for a layup they'd sing 'Stayin' Alive', which is funny – he doesn't look like Andy Gibb, though he is white and stringy. And a musician. He kept going back. To make it more fun, he sent away to America to get a chain net, rather than the empty ring or string nets that never lasted the night. He borrowed a tall ladder from Harry's *cave* in the wee hours of one morning, and walked up the canal in the moonlight to string it up. That afternoon they stopped and clapped for him when he walked on the court: *An-DY!* You have to swish, he told me, it's shit with just the ring. He hangs out with them now, and is learning their language – a mix of *verlan*, *argot*, and their own words and handshakes, a whole choreography as he arrives at a gig or walks on the court – *salut mec, ouais, en forme*. He speaks excellent street French now, but still has trouble conjugating *avoir*. Who cares, I say. What more do you need?

But he wants to know the formal language too, and tries hard to absorb what he learns at Campus Langue so he can fully function in all aspects of French society. He likes to order for us both, for example, wherever we go. One night, asking the waiter for a straw – *une paille* – he asked if he could please have a *pipe*. Which is close, but also slang for a blowjob. *Non*, said the waiter. He makes his own phone calls, stumbles through administrative procedures; when he's not sure what to say, he pouts up his lips and says *euhhh, ouaiiis, behhh* like French people do. If the conversation goes further, he says 'C*est difficile pour moi.*' I have no idea where he got this expression from and neither does he – it just comes out. *It's difficult for me.*

SOMEBODY:
Salut mec

M:
Eh, salut

SOMEBODY:
(*in fast French*)
Shot some mean baskets yesterday.

M:
(*pouting*)
C'est difficile pour moi

It's so random and sweet and self-effacing that even when it has no context it softens the situation and makes people laugh and fall in love with him. Makes me fall in love with him.

⁓

On the night of the show at La Scène Bastille, we eat dinner first with Dodger, Fanny and the band on the *terrasse* at Val's awful restaurant in Châtelet. It's become a custom to eat there as much as we can: he gives us cheap dinners laden with free extras, and endless refills of bad wine that tastes fine to us, pouring it into our glasses with apologies. One day, he is constantly saying, he'll own his own bar and we'll all drink *vin de qualité* from morning until night. He zooms around the tables like he's on speed – M says he surely is or how could he work all the way through to 7? – his deep brown eyes darting from table to table, his actor's physicality keeping him nimble as he distributes drinks and menus, manages the kitchen and bar staff, takes orders, orders waiters around, flips his dark hair out of his eyes as he leans over to pour wine. The food isn't dreadful and he keeps bringing us wine, arguing with The Dodger over an upcoming French production of *The Merchant of Venice* Val's performing in. The Dodger can't see how Shakespeare could possibly be translated.

'"Sit, Jessica", for example,' The Dodger states loudly. 'How is it possible that the phrase, "Sit, Jessica" can exist in French? It will never be the same – what about the pentameter, what about rhythm?'

'*Assieds-toi Jessica*,' says Val, collecting our plates. 'It's the similar words.'

'But not the rhythm. So not the meaning.'

'But when you seeing all the stars in the globe,' narrates Val dramatically to the sky, 'The most small star, is just singing with the angels. That's what I say!'

I have no idea what they are talking about but am glad for the distraction because I'm nervous about the show. M is fine, if a tiny bit edgy. He's done this many times, but never in Paris, and never as the leading man. The warm-up shows at Espace B and the Flèche d'Or went fine, but this is the one that could launch his career here. He was fantastic in those smaller shows, entertaining the small crowds with his imperfect French, telling stories about the album and playing his fragile, scratchy guitar with us behind him swelling the songs into soundscapes that seem to take off into their own lands, but are perfectly scripted and directed by M. My playing has gotten better and I don't need the sticky notes as much on my keyboard. Annick had to go back to Canada so M found a young Marseillais called Jean-Yves to play bass and Dan moved to drums. No luck with finding a lead guitarist, nobody had the subtlety that M's old band mate had when he recorded the tracks in New York. We had to resign ourselves to the fact those melodies would not exist, which is painful for me because on the record they're hypnotic. M is fine about it. Welcome to rock 'n roll, he said. Always problems, things never working, band mates dropping out and moving away. At the first show he met a vibraphonist – a jazz dude – who asked if he could play with us. A trombonist almost made it on too, but it didn't work. There was one Italian guy named Emiliano who *almost* made it as lead guitarist but when it came close to the show he couldn't help himself, started bending notes like wild, *weooow, weeeowwwww*. M was patient, gave him a few goes, then elegantly fired him.

Val wipes his hands and runs off to get changed to walk with us to La Scène. The group grows along the way, Charles, Harry, Hanne, Nadine and Didier, the night is freezing and feels like it could snow. Franck is waiting for us outside the venue, and kisses M and I on both cheeks. M is calm. Dan is fidgety. The bassist turns up in red leather pants. As the first band plays and the place fills up, Franck introduces M to the industry people he has invited – film people, booking agents, tour managers, producers. He has arranged a sexy French chick with wild dreadlocks to sell the merch M has had made: vinyl and CDs and t-shirts with the strange guy on the horse from the album cover. I'm not sure I look right; I've pinned my hair up and am wearing a silk shirt and high heels with the scarf Mondrian gave me high and tight around my neck. When it's time for us to take the stage, M is in his element, talking to the crowd and playing like he's always been here. I play as carefully as I can to protect his vision, fingers shaking. I can't see my texta marks on the keyboard in the darkness but I manage to remember the notes and play the feelings behind the songs that M has written as best I can. Everything goes smoothly. Nothing catches fire, nobody falls on a glass, nobody pulls their pants down.

The show is a success. Franck hooks M up with a booking agent in Paris and agrees that a showcase in LA and NYC is a good idea. He sets about helping M arrange a small tour in March, tying the two shows – and possibly another in Austin – in with my friend Gabriella's wedding. A new American label is interested in putting the album out in the States and offers to pay for our flights and accommodation in America. M is over the moon.

We host an orphan's Christmas at Annelets. M cooks a chicken and a turkey and vegetables in the disgusting oven on which I have tried every nuclear cleaning product to de-scunge. I tell myself the years of baked-in fat and the fumes it gives off won't affect our glorious fare. Because we celebrate on the 25th rather than the evening before, as the French do, Valentin, Fanny and Didier can come. Charles has been conscripted. Harry comes with two sixpacks of *Kro*.

Nadine comes in the morning to help, impressed with how we've made the dive a home. It's true, it almost is. I've put up my collages and filled the crooked bookshelves with objects I've gathered and books I've slowly been collecting or loaned. I bought some cheap crockery and plates from a sale at Habitat and M and I have been having fun picking up little odds and ends from the janky *vide-greniers* around these parts where things are still 20 centimes.

The solitude of last Christmas compared to the messy conviviality of this one makes me happy. M asked me to list one of the traditional things we had at home at Christmastime and I told him about the terrible soft lollies that came in a giant bag mixed with salted nuts; the salt would go all over the sweet lollies and make them all taste hideous, but that for me was the taste of Christmas. Now he has placed a salted lolly/nut mix in small wicker baskets along the kitchen bench, to be eaten prior to, during or after the meal – all day – to give that special sickly Christmas feeling in your guts, that furry tongue. He doesn't understand this. His family sounds more sane. I notice that the nuts and sweets he's bought are nothing like the cheap ones we had at home, they are Haribos and dried fruits and dry-roasted *noisettes*, which probably cost a fortune.

So it's not the same, but everyone enjoys them in a slightly confused way, as we sit cross-legged on the floor, and I've thrown a cloth over the kids' table and lit candles and we sit eating and drinking all afternoon and everything is joyful that day and the next and the next and the next.

Until February.

The Boy

A boy is dead.

Decapitated by an *ascenseur.*

I receive the email in the late afternoon.

The email is from Harry.

Subject: *PARIS: ADOLESCENT DÉCAPITÉ PAR ASCENSEUR*

Jayne,

Did you see this in today's *Parisien*?

I hope you're sitting down.

Harry x

PS <u>Do NOT read the comments.</u>

A few minutes before the kick-off of the Portugal–Germany match last Thursday night, a 14-year-old boy left his neighbour's apartment to go upstairs and tell his mother he'd be watching the game with his friends downstairs. As he walked up the ancient stairwell of the 1930s building in Paris' 17th arrondissement, one of his friends called out to him from one of the lower floors. The boy looked over the stairwell banister to respond to him without realising he had actually put his head in the lift well. A lift was descending. The teenager was instantly killed, his head torn off by the lift cabin.

I shut the computer then open it again.

A 1930s building. No protection between the staircase and the elevator shaft. Boy looks over. A railing of 1.7 metres vertically, barely 1 metre on a slight angle from some stairs. Same as in Sophie's building. Two years ago, the article says, OPAC, the Public Housing Office in Paris, launched a vast renovation project for pre-war lifts. This elevator had already been renovated, but not the protection around the cage. Were the lifts supposed to have been fully enclosed by now? Does Hogarth know this?

"It was not his habit to lean over. We knew it was dangerous and we often told our little brothers, sisters and nieces to be very careful," said his 13-year-old cousin, still in shock.

"When we take the stairs with a small one, we stick to the wall because we know very well that it is risky," said a resident.

Do NOT read the comments.

COMMENTAIRES:

I live in this kind of building – and I notice the non-respect of safety by the young – they slam doors, climb in the lift eight at a time – how many deaths have happened since these lifts were put in service? Of course the death of this kid is sad – but why didn't the mother tell him about the dangers of these lifts – he climbed on the cage to put his head over and we look to the State or OPAC as responsible – no I don't agree – even if the family is of Magrebin origin, they knew the dangers ...

So sad for this kid! The lift wasn't up to current standards, but strangely there had never been an accident before. So can someone explain to me how suddenly this boy managed to put his head through the cage? At 14, isn't one aware of the dangers of lifts?

Horrible.

The poor kid, he was so young.

The gore – I feel bad for the people that saw it.

I'm in shock! Poor kid.

As long as there are people who think that old places are cool to live in, there'll be super cool accidents, in the same style as their cool apartments.

It seems these deadly elevator accidents only happen to immigrant kids.

He was not an immigrant, he was French, of Magrebin descent.

These open lifts are illegal.

They are not illegal – the deadline to bring them up to the new safety standards was pushed back two years …

I do not understand why one would wait to renovate his elevator! A quarter of them are over fifty years old, how do you expect them to be up to current safety standards.

I'm grossed out, bad.

I decide to do the lawsuit.

The Actress Prepares

'I think you should run.'

'Nah,' says M.

'But it'll be awful. I'll be awful. Why don't you go and have a fun time with a sweet Parisian chick without this stupid baggage.'

'I don't want to do that. I would if I did. But I don't.'

'I think you're mad. I think you should go and live your life.'

'I am living my life. And it's not like life will stop because of the lawsuit.'

'I mean without this drag.'

'Strange as it may sound, none of this is a drag. And please don't think you know what it is I want. That is not your business.'

It's almost a reprimand. I pull my head in.

The lifts were supposed to have been improved. The improvements had been delayed two years. If they were at the new standard, my accident would not have happened. The boy would not have lost his life.

Would they keep delaying the renovations? How could this happen, after what happened to me? Will they do something to stop this happening again?

I feel responsible.

Is it reasonable to hope that someone might address this, in some way? Normal even? I'm not trying to prove something to Paris or to take my near-death experience out on the city, I'd just like to make sure that the buildings know that people can be decapitated and to make sure the protections are good enough that people don't die. Now. Before it happens again. To not take legal steps would deny the fact that the accident happened, and could happen to someone else, and now it has happened, to the boy. It's not about money, though that had been a tantalising thought at first. Money just seems to be the only thing that makes people sit up and listen, make change.

If I don't do something, will anything be done?

I don't want to be a victim. I'm not a victim. I lived. I can move. My face is not that bad. I think there's something a bit wrong with my ear and the feeling in parts of the right side of my face hasn't come back, but whatever. I'm here. My god, sweet boy, I want to take you by the hand. I would be with you right now if not for that lift in Sophie's building stopping when it did. I don't understand why I'm here and you are not.

I understand you, boy. That feeling that you just want to *grab* life. The game was happening, you were disoriented with excitement, I will think of you always. Killed in a flight of enthusiasm. I know you're fine, I know it would have been so fast and you were gone. It's your mum I think of. The way they describe the sound she made in the article. I can't translate that here on the page.

I won't let it get in.

I'll do the right thing.

M will help, he says. He understands these procedures.

He says the key to it is to frame it well in your mind. To see the lawsuit as a job. It's not your life. Not you. Just a checklist to tick off.

If you can find a way to go on with your life, he tells me, and do the lawsuit on the side, you will be able to get through it. We can pick away at it together like a project. Keep it outside of yourself, don't let it in, don't invest emotionally. There'll be a lot of hard stuff to do – paperwork – it will be tough. You should expect it to drag on forever. You must try not to have high expectations.

I think just doing it is my expectation, I tell him.

He tells me that's smart. And he will be with me every step of the way.

I thank him.
He hugs me tight.

⁓

There's not much choice other than to go with Hogarth. He takes a small fee up front, that Dad has kindly offered to pay. There will be other expenses to be paid to the experts, he tells us, but in dribs and drabs.

HOGARTH:
Okay, let's work out the nitty gritty.
(*he takes out my file, a fountain pen and branded stationery*)
You will need to ask your ... ex-fiancé – Adrien Masson – for
his *témoignage*. He was there with you in the hospital on the
night of the accident, yes? It's very important to have his account.
Send that to me first. Just a simple statement of what he saw
that night.

A mix of dread and old desire coagulates in my gut.

JAYNE:
Okay.

HOGARTH:
You will need a <u>stack</u> of *témoignages* – from psychiatrists,
surgeons, physio, evidence about your career before the
accident, people you work with as an actor, saying your
career is kaput, your agent, your theatre school, all the health
professionals. Also from your social security in Australia,
the *sécu* here, lists of all the amounts you've paid, letters
from your father, your sister, your friends, the woman in the
building you were visiting ... I'll send you a full list but here's
a start. It won't be easy doing this. Are you strong enough?

I nod.

HOGARTH:

I need you to understand – when you ask people for the
témoignages, you will need to ask them to exaggerate their
accounts of how bad the accident has affected you, that your life
is hopeless now, you are disfigured, you are messed up,
changed, it's all over, you'll never be the same …

JAYNE:

But that's not true. I'm dealing with it okay.

HOGARTH:

That's not the point. We have to *illustrate* it this way, or they
won't pay attention. You have to see it as a hypothetical. What
would a young actress's life be, post a trauma like this?

JAYNE:

I don't want to ask people to lie.

HOGARTH:

They're not lying. They're exaggerating the truth, for a just cause.

JAYNE:

The idea of that makes me ill.

HOGARTH:

Then you have no case. Go out and live your life,
everything's okay.

JAYNE:

But it's not.

HOGARTH:

So there, you have a job to do. Ask your boyfriend to help you.
He knows the way this stuff works. It's just the legal system.

If you want them to listen, and for change to occur, you need
to paint the picture clearly.

JAYNE:
Okay.

HOGARTH:
Good, well get going then, and gather your strength. You'll have
to go to Salpêtrière and collect the hospital file and bring it to me
immediately. And your theatre school, agent … good. And send
through all the other things as soon as you can.

JAYNE:
Okay. I'm seeing my *kiné* today.

HOGARTH:
Yes, one from him too. And, of course, you'll need to be here
for the hearing. They'll do a psychiatric report, physical, and of
course the lift *expertise*. You're in Paris now permanently?

JAYNE:
Yes.

HOGARTH:
Good, you will need to be here. You will be busy. It will be like
preparing for a role, getting into character.

JAYNE:
Except this did happen …

HOGARTH:
I know, I know but you know what I mean. Now don't go back
to Australia or anything, that would be expensive, and stupid.
You'll need to be contactable at all times.

JAYNE:
So, I will need to be physically present for all this?
It won't just be paperwork …

HOGARTH:
No no no. It's all about your presence. It's a *show*. It's a good idea
for you to try to see it that way, use your training. Or you'll go
mad or get depressed.

JAYNE:
But how do I tell the difference between what is a show
and what is real?

Tears spring up in my eyes, I wipe them away furiously.

HOGARTH:
Well now, let's not go into metaphysics. Just look after yourself
and stay strong. See that *kiné* person and keep active.

I stand to leave.

JAYNE:
Thank you for seeing me and for taking this on.

HOGARTH:
It's your funeral! Well, fortunately not. Ha! Now go and let me set
about winning this for you. Don't forget your friend, whatsizname,
the Frenchy – email him. First off the rank, though, Salpêtrière.

The word sends shivers down my spine.

Evidence

Detective Tuttle: Morbid Private Investigator.

Before I do anything else, there is something I need to see. It makes me sick but when M's at the track I walk to the rue Saint-Maur and take the line 3 to Malesherbes, my old au pair métro stop, the boy's métro stop. The clean, upright *quartier* welcomes me back. It feels different now, tainted, not the innocent place I knew, the buildings looking down on me like they're laughing, like they have a dirty secret they'll never share with me. Murder has happened, they're all suspects, but they don't care, standing there in their glory, beauty admired by all. I check the map and walk down the boulevard, turn right, then left, then right again, and then I'm there. In a leafy square. Outside the boy's building.

I had planned to wait outside, steal my way in, get a look at the lift, take notes on my pad. See what had changed since the boy's death, see if his lift was in any way similar to mine.

But I don't need to do this. The building, quiet in front of me in the freezing air, is almost a carbon copy of Sophie's in the rue Pelleport. Unusual for Paris, with its red-gold brick exterior and art-deco features; a warm and welcoming murderess. The boy would have played here with his friends in the square each day, climbed the stairs or taken the lift to his apartment, run up and down and out and in since he was small.

His cousins nearby, his school down the road, perhaps he took the bus or the métro, was he a good student? From his photo he was a kind boy, a sporty boy, a gentle son.

In the paper, the photos of the stairwell and his lift looked just like Sophie's, but I wanted to see it for myself. Now I don't need to. What am I doing here? What if I met his family in the building, or even out here? I hadn't thought of that, as though the building would be abandoned. I feel unsteady, my knees about to give way, and rush to a nearby bench and crouch down. Breathe. Then I get out of the square as fast as I can.

How many more buildings are there like this?

Back at Annelets I look on the internet. Plenty of beautiful 1930s buildings in Paris come up, but nothing like Sophie's and the boy's. This is some relief, though I know it's far from a definitive search.

These sorts of lifts were added to the buildings in the 1950s. Paris was not built with lifts in mind. When Napoleon III asked Baron Haussmann to redesign the cramped, collapsing city in the 1850s, to 'aerate, unify and embellish' it, he was all about staircases, and besides, the elevator had barely been invented. Then around the mid-1900s, the Parisians – or their visitors – wanted elevators and found that the box-shaped gaps between the winding stairwells would do quite nicely. Suddenly hotels had them, then fancy buildings, and then smaller, average buildings. Because the lifts nestled right up to the stairwells, protective grilles were put around the elevator shafts, either all the way from the ground floor to the ceiling, or just to banister height. The laws around them, enacted in the early 1950s, had barely been changed.

I flash back to the boy's square. Seeing his building was a valuable clue. These specific buildings have a flaw. Should I have waited and tried to see his mother? To tell her it happened to me, too? The thought chills me. Would she want to talk to me anyway? Would I want to talk to someone who survived something that had killed someone I loved?

No.

Then again, it might help the boy's family to know he wasn't the only one.

The lawsuit, if nothing else, is a means of telling them.

I flex. Prepare myself for battle.
Prepare to tick the boxes.

⁓

Hôpital de la Pitié-Salpêtrière.

Freud worked here, Josephine Baker died here, Foucault worked and died here. It was a gunpowder factory until, in the mid 1600s, Louis XIV turned it into a hospice for poor and mentally ill women, and then later a prison for prostitutes. I found a picture of an old lithograph by an artist called Armand Gautier, showing women in the *jardins* outside the hospital illustrating the various states of madness. Their extreme poses remind me of *bouffons*, with their contorted, exaggerated shapes, or archetypes from the *commedia dell'arte*. One woman is leaning against a wall with her skirts pulled up over her head, a woman with shorn hair is wailing with her arms wrapped around her torso, another is smiling in bliss at nothing. There's an old woman begging to nobody in particular, a woman hunched over herself with a darkened face, a sinister-looking woman gesturing at something, a woman picking the grass and letting it fall. Each of them is looking at someone or something we can't see, each has an open mouth and a slack jaw. Written below are the states they represent:

Dementia
Megalomania
Acute mania
Melancholia
Idiocy
Hallucination
Erotomania
Paralysis

Most of these things I felt at some point during my stay at the Salpêtrière.

Si zéro est l'absence de douleur et dix est la douleur la plus intolerable,
quel est votre douleur?

The ancient facade looms down on me, grand and imposing. I feel small looking up at it, as small as I felt those nights when my voice must have carried down the halls like a madwoman's ghost.

S'IL-VOUS-PLAÎT?

S'IL-VOUS-PLAÎT?

Inside, the smells and sounds take me back to the angels and beautiful men with meaty faces, the grey walls so soft on my eyeballs. The ecstasy each injection would bring, making me content to lie forever in that bed and never resume life as before.

A woman directs me to a plastic chair. I sit and turn up M's music in my ears to drown out my heart racing. A deep male voice sounds above the music:

DEEP MALE VOICE:
Mademoiselle Tootle?

Belmondo. I recognise his meaty face, which is not beautiful at all. He is wearing a pale grey suit to match his grey, sunken eyes. He smells lightly of smoke. He ushers me into his office, looking me up and down with a serious look on his face.

BELMONDO:
You look like you have healed well. Take off your scarf, please.

I reluctantly unwind the thick winter scarf, so soft with wear it feels part of my neck. I close my eyes, which helps the world slow down. He lightly touches the back of my neck, asks me to look left, right, up and down, to bend over and touch my toes. He feels the front of my neck, my glands, checks my pulse.

BELMONDO
Okay mademoiselle Tootle, c'est bon.

I open my eyes. He asks about Bérénice and the check-ups and Australia, and draws a sharp breath when I mention the chiropractor. I tell him about the medication and the Cage and he says he's glad I'm feeling better and that I should call him if I need any help. He asks why I need the medical file though he knows already so I explain it to him again, I need it for the lawsuit as I'm issuing a complaint against the building. He pushes a thick red folder towards me with a stern look and wishes me *courage*. Before I leave I ask if he can thank Noémie for me. Noémie? The nurse. He isn't sure what I'm talking about.

⌇

I have made a list of all the people we need statements from. Or rather, I have drawn them from my flesh, writing down those closest to me in order to harass them about the accident, remind them of what they have been through and ask them to write terrible things about me. M writes a generic letter for me and asks if I'd like to see it, saying it's better if I don't. I say no, and thank you so much for doing this. I could not do it without him. A terrible pressure on this fragile thing we have, but he assures me he is fine with it, it's like a small side-job, too easy. I give him the addresses and let him send the emails out and make the calls. He tells me my part of that job is now over. Box ticked. He will gather the letters up and send them to Hogarth. He has spoken with Hogarth and advised him that he will be handling that side of things. Hogarth thinks this is a good idea, the letters can be very upsetting, and need to be in fact, in order to convince the tribunal. If in English, all the letters will need to be translated into French, which will cost quite a bit of money. It's okay, M tells him, we have the money to pay for the translations now. M tells me he has started a file where the letters will go and that I won't see it. It is better that way.

It feels terrible to be involving M in this dreadful process, we've barely known each other a year. It disturbs me that *he* is going to read these letters, about how hopeless I am now, how badly I've been hurt, how my career is ruined. He never knew me before, how does he even know who I am, who I was, to compare it to? It disturbs me that we have to go to this level in order to convince an insurance company that something should be done about this. It seems bizarre and barbaric. M assures me again and again it's a game, not to invest in it. 'Ignore it all,' he says. 'I am more aware of the game than you are. I won't read the letters logically either – in fact I don't plan to look at them. Let's ignore it all now. The hearings and assessments will be the hardest part, you need to save your energy for those.'

I have written my own letter to Adrien, asking for his statement. The email is calm and measured and trying not to come across as distant, though if not an amorous exchange, anything we write feels stone cold. I don't know how to address him or sign off, I only called him Adrien and he only called me Jayne when we were furious with each other. I wrote *Cher Adrien* and signed off *Amitiés*, Jayne. Friendship. I toyed with *Amitiés sincères*, but simple 'friendship' sounded less false than sincere friendship.

His response comes as I'm typing ideas for a slogan for a dog weight-loss brand beside sleeping M. Do people really put their dogs on diets? The bed has become my office; I am trying not to wear the scarf anymore, though it's cold and I can easily justify it. Bed is the most comfortable place I know to work, where I can prop my lower back up to take the pressure off my neck. When it's particularly bad I put on the Aspen collar, but not for long, and never in front of M. Best is no brace or scarf. My head feels giant. Bérénice insisted my neck is stronger and I need to let the muscles regain their strength, which I know is true, but when I first ventured out without wearing the scarf I was struck by how little it was about the pain anymore, more the sense of protection it provided from random death coming at any moment, from any angle. Classic PTSD, of course, anyone could diagnose that.

Seeing Adrien's name makes my gut clench. I don't want to open the email straight away, and lie looking at M's face, the picture of peace. My little friend. My *petit ami*. I thought Adrien was my friend. On the night of the accident he was the first one I asked for. Sophie asked me for his number which I knew like I knew my name, but I couldn't remember it. Then he was there, he was always there, I knew though we had ended it he'd be by my side. He sat with me in ambulances and through the hospital halls and the terror of those moments in the stark cold room with the medicine charts on the wall, and he was there when they told me I'd broken my neck and he watched the doctor pull the flesh of my cheek away to examine the depth of the cut beneath it and my peachy skin doubled back to touch my own peachy skin. He was there, learning his lines for his audition, for the hours that it took the doctor to stitch me up, he was there afterwards to kiss me goodbye. And then he never returned. I moaned his name in those long nights as the Love peaked and waned, my friend, my family, the only one I wanted to see. I remember meeting him not long before the accident, after I'd moved to the rue de la Chine. We had decided to see each other one last time, to give each other back a few last things, and to be sure it was done and see if we could still be friends. He suggested we meet at the Bar des Amis, high on Montmartre, where we used to go on Sunday afternoons, after roaming the streets and markets, to huddle over beers and hot wine in winter or rosé in summer, and kiss and talk and plan. We sat that day in a cold corner, unsure what to say. Afterwards we walked outside and the snow disappeared us before we could truly say goodbye. Bar des Amis means Friends' Bar. I don't think that's what we were.

Subject: *Témoignage*

M stirs, I hurry to read the email before he wakes up.

Chère Jayne. My heart pounds, that same sick mix of sex and adrenalin I've had any time we've had contact since the accident. If he is to be honest, he writes, he has a little 'case of conscience', regarding the trial, of *vénale* intention from his point of view. Which, however, is none of his concern, he says, and is not for him to judge. The way he writes is so distant and formal I wonder if someone else has written it for him. Though I'm sure at his fancy boys school they taught him to write such letters. The responsibility for some things, he says, has to be taken upon ourselves. But if he must, he will write the statement most formally, and as I have asked him for this service, he should therefore have the right to express himself on how he feels about the situation. It would be the same, for example, as if he had asked me to pay for the phone calls he made to my family on the night of the accident. He would therefore like to receive a letter from my lawyer, evoking what HE expects from him in a clear and formal way. And to conclude, he would like to be sure that I understand it will be my friends, Sophie, Frédéric and Lou, that will be paying the price for these proceedings. We must take responsibility for our own actions. *Sincèrement.* Adrien.

My stifled emotion makes a small choking sound.

'*Chérie!*' says M, rubbing his eyes. '*Tout est okay?*'

'Yep. Just these dirty dogs!'

'Less weight, more life, is genius,' he says, referring to the slogan he came up with last night.

He gets up and I wait until he's in the shower to write an angry email back to Adrien saying thanks a lot and asking if his bank details are the same for me to wire the fifty cents.

In the coming days I reread and reread the email. The word that sticks out the most is *vénale*. Venal, in English. According to the thesaurus: bitter, corrupt, mercenary, bent, crooked.

Vénale against whom? Sophie? His culture?

He thinks it's my fault. He thinks I should have been more careful. Perhaps he thought I was suicidal, that I wanted to do something crazy. He was always telling me to slow down, be more careful, crazy butterfly. Can you suicide without meaning to?

I'm too ashamed to show the email to M. He'll discover Adrien is right, I'm a dirty, crooked, mercenary bitch that did it to herself, deserved it.

I forward Adrien's email to Hogarth, instructing him to please make a formal request.

⁓

Was it suicide? I don't think I wanted to die that night, but I can't be sure.

When I was little and the world was asleep and I felt like the only one alive, I would get this dreadful feeling I called the cold feeling, and when that feeling came it would reassure me to think that I could die too, and if I could make myself die, then list the reasons not to:

- because there are choc tops
- because a leaf might fall on my head
- because Jenny's in my class

It was a fun game and easy because there were so many things I loved. It helped me sleep.

When I got older and the cold feeling returned, I would think 'why not kill myself today'? And make the list:

- because we might be getting a guinea pig
- because Malt-o-Milks
- because high jump

And I got through Grade Four fine. Just being aware that my life was in my own hands had a powerful, positive effect on me. It made every aspect of the world seem more special and heightened than ever. It also made a lot of sense. It was the only thing we knew for certain. So why not start there and work backwards?

Death was my comfort. And I saw thinking of suicide as a positive thing, because I never really had a moment that I didn't want something from the world, or anything that I wasn't curious to stay and discover. When life was great it would prevent complacency, every tiny detail in life becoming magnified because in comparison to death and eternal nothingness, a single breath is sublime.

189

- because I just figured out how to give myself an orgasm
- because I could go to Paris or India or Brazil
- because my hair might be good tomorrow

The closest I got to actually going through with it was after Mum died. Her disappearance coloured every reason to live meaningless. I didn't see how anything could be enjoyed ever again without her presence on the planet.

Then the scholarship to Paris dropped from the sky, the residency at the Récollets. In Paris the colour of the world was so different, a new life began.

On that dark night of January 18, I don't remember specifically thinking about death as I sat against the cold wall of the apartment in the rue de la Chine, or listing the reasons to live, or feeling like there was no point in going on. I do remember being in a certain state. Tired. Sad. But alight.

I wasn't thinking of dying. But perhaps my body did the work for me.

Perhaps it *was* me.

But then I think of the boy. If I accept that it was my fault or subconscious desire, then I imply it was the boy's, too. A 14-year-old boy about to watch the Portugal–Spain match does not wish to die by decapitation.

⁓

HOGARTH:
They're throwing everything they've got at you.

Hogarth is very animated today, like he's had too much coffee. His thick flick of silver hair bounces as he talks and changes direction.

JAYNE:
Really? Gosh.

HOGARTH:

I'm not surprised. Well, a little surprised at the virulence
of their *réplique*. However, I knew they wouldn't simply hand
over the money like some group of Americans.

JAYNE:

I just – the fact that it *happened*. I'm surprised they'd be so *mean*.

I never know how to be in his presence; whether I should be playing
my role of damaged person, or if I should be presenting myself as his
colleague on this project, or if I just am a damaged person. The role I
end up playing is a wrestle between child, partner, victim and defendant.
A *soupe*, Claude would say.

HOGARTH:

Oh yes. Regardless of the boy, they are, and will be, as
mean as possible to stop you doing this thing.

JAYNE:

Oh.

HOGARTH:

Let's look at their email together.

He pulls a chair up next to me and opens his laptop, slamming it shut
again as though remembering to add a touch of humanity.

HOGARTH:

Needless to say, their allegations are as contemptuous as
they are unfounded.

JAYNE:

Okay. Thanks.

He translates the email to me, though I assure him I understand.

The tribunal must not be deceived by the pretentions 'à l'Américaine' of Madame Tuttle or by her excessively overblown attempts to enrich herself via these proceedings.

Woah.

The complainant was only in hospital for a week.

Yeah, because my sister is a nurse and came to Paris to care for me until I was able to get a plane back home, then my dad cared for me.

It is established that the complainant, knowing the building at 26-28 rue Pelleport perfectly well, mounted the staircase while her friend was entering the building. She climbed the protective grille, which was fully in line with the height laws of 1951, to call out to her friends below.

CLIMBED? I DID NOT CLIMB!

The elevator's installation, maintenance and conformity to the law was in perfect order, and did not deviate from its route, or present any dysfunction of any kind. The expert confirms that on the day of the visit to the building, the elevator was in perfect accordance with the law of 1951. It is clear that Madame Tuttle put herself in danger by leaning over.

The law of 1951!

The completely irrational behaviour of Madame Tuttle is what created this occurrence and she is entirely responsible for the consequences, by putting herself off balance and placing her weight on her hands, raising herself into the lift cage and inserting her head directly into the path of the elevator. The tribunal will conclude that Madame Tuttle, by putting her head into the void, had voluntarily displayed a comportment that was not only dangerous and at fault, but unpredictable and responsible for the payment of the legal fees accumulated here.

My breath is short.

She has lost no income.
She had no job when the accident occurred.
There is no need for ongoing therapy.
Her eventual loss of income is quasi-imaginaire, *but despite this she demands the reimbursement of a star!*

Okay, maybe that last one is fair.

Hogarth slams the laptop shut.

HOGARTH:
That's only part of it. Can you handle it?

JAYNE:
Give it to me.

He re-opens the computer.

The fault of the victim constitutes the exclusive cause of the accident.

Fuck off.

Jayne Tuttle committed the fault of leaning over the protection rails of the elevator shaft to speak to her friend and to see the little girl.

The current regulations with regards to the height of the protections were respected, so the accident could only have occurred due to the irresponsible and dangerous conduct of the victim.

Mean.

Madame Tuttle knew perfectly well that a lift moved up and down the middle of the stairwell, and she admitted such by saying 'I never

take the lift because Mme Pasteur lives on the second floor and it's
not high.'

I said it after the fact you dipshit.

Madame Tuttle knew the lift was there because she saw the lift cables
unrolling before her eyes.

WHAT?

Madame Tuttle climbed the protective grille to put her head over the void.

Did not!

Dangerous, irresponsible, and going against all simple good sense.

Maybe but fuck you anyway.

Madame Tuttle presents herself as a grand artiste, which was a surprise to
the Tribunal. In fact at the time of the accident she was nothing more than
a part-time teacher and student. Her career in theatre is a hobby, not a
well-paid career.

MEAN!

The tribunal will thereby state and judge Madame Jayne Tuttle completely
responsible for the accident of which she was victim.

JAYNE:
Sorry!

I make it to the bathroom in time to splash Hogarth's porcelain with the
morning's *escargot* from Du Pain et des Idées.

Nadine calls as I leave Hogarth's, asking how I am and where I've been lately. I tell her I've been busy with copywriting, but it's the lawsuit making me want to be a recluse, even from M, which makes me sad, and him too, though he is good at not showing it. I keep ending up at Marie-France's – she is very pregnant now and in a constant bad mood, which is good to be around. She's been working on the script, which has finally been submitted and Antoine is very happy with it. He keeps asking me up to the 20th to watch the development and be involved but I make an excuse each time. When I try to think of going up there my mind blocks it out, like that area has been blanked out of the map and in my mind. It's infuriating and embarrassing and stupid and dramatic. But it's a physical impossibility. My legs won't go.

'Everything is *heavy*, mother*fuck*,' moans Marie-France. 'My feet, my belly, my brain. Hakim *le salaud*, he just goes on working, in his life, like nothing is happening. I can't do *anything* – I'm a big ball of shit.'

She has some kind of condition that makes her swell and makes walking painful. She has needed to lie down a lot because she is in danger of premature birth or miscarriage. She's close to her due date now and the danger has passed but it's left her almost entirely physically incapacitated. I've been teaching her new English expressions I've mostly made up, to give her more range for her vast emotions.

'Dickshit *putain de* fuckedy fuck. In a jar. How are you feeling?'

She knows everything except the story of the boy – I spare her that much in the state she is in. She is vehement that I should sue the building anyway, she always has been. Today she is doing paperwork for her social security, *cunt-ache*. I cuddle up on her bed and tell her about the arguments from the other side, the letters I'm not seeing. She rants as she makes tea about the French, the French administration, the city, the whole *putain de société*. I can't help but laugh at the angry words coming through her delicate French mouth.

'At least you're getting out of here for a moment.'

Our flight leaves tomorrow for LA, for the wedding and four shows – or *showcases* – with the band. It's perfect timing. The idea of leaving this all behind for a moment fills me with light.

'Take me with you?' says Marie-France. 'The old me? I can leave this belly here for a few weeks, it will be fine.'

She sits down and starts crying. I hug her. I remember how perfect I thought she was at theatre school, how graceful and lithe and Parisian. How much I wanted to be her. Now she is so real. The balletic waif replaced with a blotchy, sweating mass. Her face is puffy and her hair thick and wiry, and she has marks on her forehead like someone flicked coffee on her. She keeps talking about the *péridurale* and the *clinique* and the *sage-femme* and then getting angry at what she's talking about.

I feel bad I'll likely miss the birth, but she has planned it meticulously like an operation and says she won't need anyone.

'Hakim is coming over, *fils de pute*,' says Marie-France, tossing her phone on the sofa.

I hug her and go to the door.

'When I get back from America there'll be two people here, not one!'

She sighs. 'Yes.'

America

M, Texas Dan, Marseille Jean-Yves and I fly overnight to LA and lifting above France is like ascending into heaven. I can see it now down there, earth, dirt, life. A hit of perspective that is quickly forgotten with in-flight movies, the sharing of headphones – have you heard this? – and many visits from the flight attendant bearing drinks. Pete, the new label guy, meets us at the airport and drives us in a rental van straight to a burger joint where he is careful to order a burger with no lettuce nor tomato in it. He is a pale, chubby guy from Texas and he says he never eats vegetables. He takes us to a hotel where we have a few days in a nearby studio before the showcase at a place in Hollywood called the Knitting Factory.

LA is exactly how I'd imagined, like the suburbs back in Australia but bigger and trashier and far more fun. Gabriella meets us on the second morning in a diner and surprises us by ordering her breakfast in a full American accent, saying they can't understand her if she speaks Australian and it gets tiring. The wedding is in a week and she's ecstatic to meet M and ecstatic that we've come. She fits into LA so perfectly with her doll-perfect hair and figure-hugging clothes. She was always the one at drama school in Melbourne most likely to succeed. We sound-check that afternoon and though my keyboard dies and Pete only just makes it back on time and I have no time to write all my instructions on the keys, the show is full and we all play well and a lot of albums get sold by Pete at the door. M says it might take a while for anything to catch on and after all, it is an instrumental band, so don't get excited.

I'm just thrilled to have left the weight of Paris and the lawsuit behind. I miss it the moment we land, but the world of diners and highways and bright beaming sunshine is the ideal distraction and my shoulders fall, my body threatening to relax but my mind not allowing it – it's as though it's afraid that in letting go my bones will fall in a pile on the ground. I know it is coming, I know the lawsuit is the key to allowing some of this tension to fall away. Answers will help. A response from Paris. I'm sure I'll be able to let go then.

In the meantime, new surroundings with no danger of pot plants or stairwell guillotines or Adrien on posters is doing me good. And M's music is the focus, which makes everything light. It's my first time in America and he is keen to make me love it, so I get the royal tour of the hotels and rooftop pools and after-gig parties, his favourite diners and record shops.

The guys fly to Austin before us, so we can stay an extra two days in LA for the wedding. Gabriella's family have put us up in a hotel with a giant fishtank inserted into the wall behind the reception desk with women lying in it. The maid of honour is a Hollywood superstar and has rented the bungalow where John Belushi killed himself, which Gabriella and her friends state like it's a badge of honour while holding their champagne glasses. I don't know how to be. I got a bad dye job in Paris and I'm self-conscious about my scar and Mondrian's scarf and my pale, wasted limbs, so I slather myself in fake tan which makes me stink and look like an orange. I wear a vintage hat that covers my right cheek to the wedding and I'm sure I look stupid and the superstar says as we wait together for the toilet *You're beautiful*, and I'm not sure how to take it and say back 'are you *serious*, look at you' and she gets offended and I realise later that as the superstar she's allowed to give compliments but we're not allowed to give them back because it's so evident that she is gorgeous, a fact reiterated by the whole wide world. I think my response might have been subordination. M gives me a funny look from the other side of the table, where he has been plonked in a bunch of buff dudes, according to the place settings, 'to mix things up'. He looks hilariously out of place in the bronzed bodies, with his pale skin and wispy hair. I feel like a mushroom. Marcus and Gabriella are sweet and kind, and their families nice, but their LA friends are too shiny to relate to. Thank god M is there, as wrong as me in his dodgy suit, dancing ridiculously with Gabriella, twirling her around on the dance floor.

Marcus's dad is a lawyer and makes a beeline for me, wanting to discuss the details of my accident and the lawsuit in France. He is Australian and there's an American lawyer with him and they both work themselves into a fury over the fact that it could have happened and why I haven't simply been paid out. The two men, one with a bit of pastry in his eyebrow, compete with each other over facts and legal nuances, offering advice, reminding me how terrible the French system is and how different 'ours' is. I feel a strange sense of allegiance with the French system and though I'm engaged in a battle, I feel closer to France than Australia or America. I realise I'm not fighting the system there, in a way I'm playing a game with it. I'm trying to get to the truth. What is fair. What is *juste*. I don't want the French way of life to change. I hate the stupid extreme personal liability in the States where if you trip over a tree root someone else is responsible. Even if I think I'm doing the right thing by suing, somehow this annoying discussion has reminded me how much I love France.

After the wedding we fly to Austin to play one quick show and then to New York. M leads me up the steps at Penn Station with my eyes closed. He wants to see the look on my face when we hit the street. And there it is. My eyes fill with wonder – it's like a movie set, the yellow cabs and fire hydrants, steam coming up off the just-rained street. We've arranged to stay with his friend in the West Village, who gives us his small single bed to sleep in while he sleeps on his couch. Sean is moving back to Austin at the end of the year – the rent is too much and he's tired of working in advertising to support his music career. Out in Brooklyn, the same story, the warehouse M's friends were living in has been sold and they've all scattered back to Australia, upstate, California, Michigan. After our show in the lower east side, we eat Chinese with the label guy before he heads back to Houston, and M's old band manager Michael, who says the scene is changing. Everyone's burning out, having kids, moving to where they can make music and not be under so much pressure. I think of Paris – how we can still live fairly cheap in the city – (or free!) – and still at least *make* work, whether there's a scene or not to show it in. Theatre will always live and breathe in Paris, and music will always be there, even if the city ain't rock. It doesn't matter, says Michael. Just live where you're happy and there'll be a place for your work.

We return to Paris with a sense of resolution.

It Puts Time

Back in Paris the mood is lighter. Spring is in full bloom. The trip seems to have put some distance on things, and I avoid M less, which he notices but doesn't say anything about. He is letting me be, and I appreciate it. Anyway, he has his own stuff going on. He goes to the track and on the days he's not there, and the evenings, starts writing a new album, *Motion Picture*. Bigger sound this time, more driving, more drums. Though there has been interest through Franck and America for film and television work and potential gigs with the first album *Here Their Dreams*, apart from a few supports and corporate gigs, and his regular Sundays at Chez Adel, there hasn't been an actual bite yet. He's not worried, the money coming in from the track (including some extra betting wins) and not paying rent makes life feel constantly abundant. Franck encourages him to keep meeting people, playing shows, getting it out there. *Ça met du temps*. It puts time.

I work too. If I focus on work I can ignore the lawsuit. More and more copywriting; now I do cat food and baby care and bathroom taps and lipstick. How many words are there for red? You'd be surprised. There's a tagline: *How many words are there for red? One. Sephora.* Damn she's good. I get a call from the biggest agency in Paris and go to the Champs-Élysées to meet them in a cold bunker-like room underground, where they explain the brief in rapid-fire French; an international cosmetics brand, years of regular work. My acting is superb. They speak too fast and give me too much information to take in but I nod and keep my mouth shut, wearing my glasses though I don't need them, my new lightweight black scarf. They'll send the brief by email anyway, I'll read it later. I'm playing the game, the role, the person they want to see. Good preparation for the role ahead, I figure. Good preparation for being a real adult.

I finally do a short reading at the English bookshop after delaying the date over and over again. M, Nadine and I grab a quick *croque* at Penis, before heading over to the reading room. My legs are jelly. Several writers are reading ten minutes of their work, which is perfect for me, I don't have much I'm happy with. A lot of it is about Adrien, in embarrassing detail, but M convinced me to read it anyway, not to censor myself. I asked how he'd feel if I was reading a story to the public about the vein in *his* cock? He shrugged and said the only issue would be all the chicks that would come looking for him. I asked if he would mind if I ever wrote about him and he said of course not. What if I write shit about you that's not true? I wouldn't care, he said, as long as you didn't use my actual name. What if I did use your actual name? Well, it would depend on the quality of the writing. What if the writing was shit? Well then that would come back on you. So, if I made the writing excellent and trashed your name you wouldn't mind. I'd probably simply rather you called me someone else. Like Trevor? Not like Trevor. What name would you choose for yourself? He thought about this. Dave? I suggested. Pete? God no. What name then? I don't know. That's your job as the artist.

The reading is fun; about forty of us crammed into the upstairs library with its window looking out over the trees in full spring blossom, Notre-Dame, the Seine, a warm breeze blowing through the window as I read. People listen, murmur, cough, Nadine laughs at the parts she recognises, and the bookseller's daughter hands me piece of paper afterwards with some suggestions of agents and publishers on it. The bookseller, seated up the back in his worn velvet jacket, tells me to write more about Paris as he refills his yoghurt jar with wine. I want to ask what he means but he is gone.

As we walk into the street afterwards, I notice someone familiar near the used-book stand.

Sophie.

The others move off towards the bar.

SOPHIE:

I saw the notice for your reading, so I came, I hope you don't mind.

JAYNE:

Did you understand a word?

SOPHIE:

(*smiling*)

No.

I tell M and the others I'll catch up with them and walk with Sophie across to the river wall and past the *bouquinistes*.

We don't bother trying to speak English. She was terrible at it and after a few attempts at the classes imposed by her job, we gave up and just spoke French. I love the way she speaks, so fine each word seems to hang in the air, feathery notes which I always broke with my swearing and street expressions, my *quoi* at the end of sentences. She loved it, and would laugh and almost guffaw, which encouraged me to push further and seek out her *bouffon*, but in there was only flowers. She would say *mince* instead of *merde* when she dropped her pencil – *darn!* I remember asking her one night for a recommendation of somewhere romantic to take Adrien and she wrote a text message:

Les jardins du Palais Royal
À la tombée de nuit

The gardens of the Palais Royal
at the fall of night

Her delicate nature is precisely what makes what I did to her all the more brutal. The guilt is so great I haven't known how to respond to her messages asking how I am, when can we see each other. Seeing her is far less terrifying than the idea of it; I don't feel relaxed, but I don't feel like I'm going to die. It's so strange this block, even as I type this, I find it almost impossible to describe. Is it the association with death, I'm not sure. To see her, the building ... I just switch off. If I attempt to put myself in the situation of seeing her and Lou, my heart speeds up and I feel like I'm going to faint. Survival instinct? It's infuriating. Confusing. Disorienting. I am trying to understand every part of this experience but this blank, this wall, I just can't explain it logically, or even if I manage to identify it, I still can't overcome it. Sitting on this bench with the most gentle character I've ever known, it's absurd to feel any sort of terror. I don't, now I'm here. Her perfume is soft and powdery, and she is wearing one of the brooches she crafted. She has another little girl now, she tells me, named after a flower. I tell her I'm sorry I missed it, is she lovely? Yes, she's lovely. Lou is very well, doing good at school, she says, before her face shadows. Oh god, what did I put her through? What did she see that night when they arrived on the first floor? A nightmare. It must have marked Lou forever. I can't stand it. Imagine being four years old and walking upstairs to find the friend who was just calling out to you lying out cold in a pool of blood. I will never forgive myself for that.

They have moved to a house out in Montreuil. A bigger place, she says, as if to justify that it wasn't because of the accident. The idea of them being in a different place is comforting. Maybe I will go out and visit them there when this is all over. I think back to what Marie-France said about them coming to visit me in the hospital but then not coming in. The last time I saw them was at the rue de la Chine before I left for Australia. Lou was very scared. But she has seen that I'm okay. That is probably enough now for her to go on in her life, in Montreuil, with her little flower sister. And Sophie will tell her, after tonight, that I am fine.

I suggest taking a photo, to show Lou how well and happy I am. Completely healed, fully recovered, I just did a book reading, happy days! Sophie and I swap sides so my face is in the right light. The two of us have small pink blossoms in our hair.

Hogarth asks me to come in, today if possible. He is drinking coffee when I arrive and asks if I want one. I say yes though I don't, in his office I always feel seasick or afraid I'm going to break something. The carved chair sticks into my back. He has a small coffee maker behind his desk and hands me an espresso, which I hold in my lap. If I drink it right at the end it won't send me insane.

HOGARTH:
There's something I need to discuss with you.

JAYNE:
Yes?

HOGARTH:
Tell you, rather. First, you have been gathering the letters?

JAYNE:
Yes.

M's file with letters and statements is filling up. He is not reading them, he tells me, just glancing at them to make sure the information we need is there. But that is reading, I say. No it's not, he says. And anyway, he says, he knows how to put these things in their right compartments, I don't need to worry about it.

HOGARTH:
And you've received the dates for the hearings, yes, the medical expert and the psychiatrist?

JAYNE:
(*shifting in the chair*)
Yes.

HOGARTH:
These are just like meetings, no need for concern.

JAYNE:
Okay.

HOGARTH:
So. The last hearing has been set. The lift *expertise*, which is the assessment of the functioning of the lift, to be conducted by team of demonstrated experts, the names of whom I shall forward to you.

JAYNE:
Right. What does that involve?

HOGARTH:
Well here's the thing. It involves you – and this is an imperative, not a question – visiting the building where the accident occurred and describing, in detail, the precise events that led to the thing.

The *thing*. My hand trembles. I need to get rid of the coffee cup. I drink the bitter liquid down in a gulp. Hogarth walks over and takes the cup, placing it on his desk before pacing around the room.

JAYNE:
But – surely they can assess the building without me.

HOGARTH:
No, it is imperative that you are present. They need you to describe the events within the surroundings they occurred. There will be

engineers, people from the company that installed the lift, those who maintain it, et cetera et cetera.

JAYNE:
I can't do that.

He moves behind the desk and leans over it, splaying his hands.

HOGARTH:
Let me put it this way. If you don't appear on that day the case falls over. There is no point proceeding as of now.

I don't know how to explain that going back there feels like stepping off the planet. That to revisit that building – or even that *quartier* – is to die. I put my head in my hands. Breathe. This is beyond dramatic. It's a building. It's just stepping inside a building.

⁓

Marie-France's baby daughter Emma is very ugly. An awful thing to say about a newborn child, I know, but it's true. And I have no real qualms about saying it because I've known beautiful and handsome people with the ugliest baby photos imaginable. Adrien was one. It's almost like some people are born with an adult face they have to grow into. Anyway, with a whole life of ease ahead, free sex, people parting ways to let them through, it seems fair enough that they should suffer people baulking at them in the pram, something they won't even remember. When I tell M the secret of Emma's ugliness he laughs, and we spend a good amount of time relaying Australian expressions for ugly people:

ugly as a half-sucked mango
ugly as a dropped pie
face liked a punched lasagne
face like a smashed crab
a bulldog chewing a wasp

Though the *gynécologue* drugged Marie-France so she didn't feel a thing, baby Emma must have had some unexpected twists and turns as her face is squashed like a boxer's, her eyes are angry and her tiny uneven brow is furrowed.

But Marie-France is in love. She is an entirely different person to the ogre from the final months of her pregnancy. Though not the forest nymph she was prior to getting pregnant, she is an entirely new being, grounded, earthly, radiant. She looks up at me, holding the sucked mango, asking if I want to hold her. I say yes but I'm scared of holding something so fragile in my arms, I can't trust myself. I worry I will do something unpredictable – not drop her or hold her wrong, but swing her around by the feet or drop-kick her across the shiny floors, press my hand into that soft bit at the top of her head – I don't know why my mind keeps doing this. I pick up Emma and control my breathing, try to enjoy the human life in my arms the weight of Jean's bag of chicken. How could this have happened? This little piece of life. My pulse races and I'm suddenly terrified of dropping her.

Marie-France's mother walks into the hospital ward. Perhaps she senses my insanity because she takes the baby straight from me. We exchange greetings and niceties and Marie-France gives me her keys to water her plants. As I leave I put a wrapped gift of booties on the bed beside her.

～

The flowers on Marie-France's balcony have dried out in the heat. It's windy. I bring them inside and put some cool water in their hardened soil. Seven less potential deaths tonight.

Marie-France doesn't return to her apartment the whole summer. After the hospital she goes with the baby to Hakim's and though she always complains about how banal it is out there, he lives behind a tidy park that she can walk the pram in and breathe fresh air. Her mother makes regular trips up from the country and Hakim has a spare room for her, which is saving Marie-France, she says, from losing her mind.

She is happy out there for the moment, she says, she doesn't care about anything but Emma. She sends photos of the baby's lasagne face to me that make me smile, she is so sweet and Marie-France is so happy. Who knew a pregnancy so demonic could result in such bliss?

I find myself spending more and more time in Marie-France's apartment, a dark cloud has descended, the terror of confronting the actual effects of the accident – psychological, physical, the lift itself. It feels good to be alone and be dark rather than optimistic – not that M expects that, it is me that expects it of myself. In fact, M is the one I can be myself around the most. He doesn't expect us to be perfect and happy all the time, and for the lawsuit hanging over us to be nothing. But I want it to be nothing. I don't want to ruin things for us. So it's better to be here, where I can spit out the copywriting jobs, tap away at the book, be shit, sprawl on Marie-France's bed and stare at the ceiling, be foetal, cry, smoke even, if I want to. Whatever it takes to get through this.

Tragedian

Naked in a cubicle.
X-Ray. MRI. Bright lights. *Tournez-vous.*
Neck fracture visible. Fracture fully knitted.
Cold fingers.
Odontoid fracture
C2
Dens fracture non-displaced
Zygomatic arch fracture
Facial wound hemiface right
Partial severing of the temporal branch of the facial nerve.
Lesions to chin, below the bottom lip, right jawbone.
Cicatrices.

Doctor's assessments: complete. TICK.

Psychiatric assessment: Hôpital Lariboisière.

M doesn't come with me to this one – Hogarth thinks it will have more impact if I am alone – more pathetic. He and I wait in a sun-filled corridor, the hospital smells are comforting. They used to remind me of Mum who was a nurse, going to visit her on a shift, take her to lunch when I was at university nearby and had just got my licence.

Cement and linoleum. Aspen collar, done up tight. *Accident de ski*. My acting has been excellent lately. Switching seamlessly between roles, businesswoman, lover, casual shopper, girl who has lost everything. I can't tell which is acting and which is real. I'm the Cate Blanchett of me, award-winning, able to disappear into each of my characters. How does she do it? How does she remember all those lines?

A scrawny man in a tight grey suit who looks like Slugworth from Willy Wonka makes his way towards me.

'*Madame Tuttle?*'

'*Oui.*'

'Ah, good to see you. You are looking well.'

'Thank you,' I smile.

Hogarth pulls me aside. 'He is intimidating you. He represents the *copropriété*, the building.'

I didn't realise it would be so *Law and Order*. I resume my role, get back into character. I am very, very unwell. I am terrible. A pathetic piece of shit. I have no life. My life as I knew it is over.

The psychiatrist sits behind his heavy desk. His name is Docteur Pfeiffer. He has droopy eyes and thick dark hair and glasses that sit low on his nose. He smiles at me. I'm not sure if I'm supposed to smile back so I give him an odd grimace. I feel like I'm on trial, with my chair closest to him, six or seven men behind me including Hogarth and Slugworth. He glances over the file Hogarth has given him containing my x-rays and MRIs and medical reports and asks about my parents and what year my mother died, what year I was born, odd, factual stuff. If I veer off the facts, he interrupts me and asks another question about my life that is unrelated. Later Hogarth tells me he was checking my memory retrieval, mannerisms, lucidity, etc.

I answer the questions as simply and clearly as I can, hypothetically speaking. Hypothetically speaking I could be psychologically damaged forever from this accident. Who wouldn't be? I'm not, because I'm strong and I can get over it. But still. That is not the point of these proceedings.

I am trying to get them to admit fault, or at least most of it. They need me to act, or it will be pointless. Because I am fine. I can forget all this and move on. I don't need to be assessed, it is only because of the boy that I am here. Why *am* I here again?

'*Crises de panique?*'

I do have panic attacks. A few days ago on the métro my heart started racing for no reason and I had to come home and lie on the floor with my knees up. Because of the accident? Perhaps.

'*Cauchemars?*'

Nightmares, all the time. I've always had them. They're worse now, of course. I nearly got decapitated.

The questions are probing and endless. Do I suffer from anxiety? Nervousness? Rigidity? Depression? Flashbacks? Claustrophobia? Fear of crowds?

Sexual problems?

Yes, of course. Poor M. I have been avoiding him for months now, rigid in bed, a corpse. I had been moving more and more but since the boy and the lawsuit, my body has died. He said he understood, and not to worry, that it would come back. But it makes me sad, guilty.

Insomnia? Antisociality?

Yes. Who wouldn't have these problems after such a thing? I don't want there to be any of these problems. I can make them go, I think, for example, if I wasn't here right now I'd have a better chance of becoming sociable again, i.e., I could call Harry right now and have a drink across at the Gare du Nord and act like this is nothing but a *cauchemar*.

'Okay, that is all I need,' says Pfeiffer. He tells us to wait outside while he compiles his conclusion.

I leave the men and hide in the bathroom. The toilet stall is heaven. A woman pisses like a racehorse in the cubicle next to me, with a squeaky fart at the end that raises my spirits. Two women gossip about one of their colleagues. Different kinds of piss streams. A woman knocks, *ça va?*

The men are talking in small groups when I return to Pfeiffer's doorway. Hogarth is on a phone call. Pfeiffer calls us in. His conclusion is that Madame Tuttle is suffering post-traumatic stress syndrome. *Duh.* The date of consolidation is six months from now. It reminds me of when I saw a trainee psychologist after Mum died, and he looked in his manual and told me I could expect it to take six months to recover.

As we leave, I ask Hogarth what a date of consolidation is.

HOGARTH:

The date that you're all better and can function again
without incapacitation.

JAYNE:

But what if the psychological effects vary from person
to person over a lifetime? How do they know what will
unfold over time?'

HOGARTH:

They don't. But they need hard facts, nothing grey.
It's all just a calculation.

Hogarth is tired. I am wearing him down. I hope my performance was to his satisfaction and that he hasn't given up. He leaves and I walk towards Annelets via the Gare de l'Est and the Récollets, passing the little boy's spattering of blood , so small and faded nobody would know it's there. It wasn't the women's fault that day, just like this is not my fault. I wonder if they tried to get the man in the truck to admit fault. A sense of regret fills me at having started this, at how much time and money M and I and Dad have already spent on it, Hogarth's time and energy, but there's no going back now, or it would have all been for nothing.

M is home when I arrive, boiling pasta. He asks how it went as I sit at the kitchen bar and I tell him:

JAYNE:

Fine.

I am acting now, with M. It tears at my soul. He hands me a small bowl of pasta and we go to the couch, me sitting on the floor and slurping the food though my stomach is in knots.

JAYNE:
Two down, one to go!

He is looking in my face, trying to assess me.

I tell him about the consolidation, that everything will be fine in six months and that Slugworth tried to solicit me but that I wouldn't give out the recipe for the everlasting gobstopper.

He is unsure how to take me. All I want is to hear him talk about himself. I ask about his day and he tells me a story about how he used to say *mince!* at the basketball court when he missed a shot – he must have thought it was the right thing to say because he hears me say it sometimes, ironically mimicking Sophie. Which is hilarious – like saying 'darn it!' on the basketball court. Anyway, the boys at the court would laugh and one day the tall one told him you say *putain de merde* when you're annoyed. Then tonight in the Franprix he was buying a sixpack of beer and one fell out and rolled behind the register and M said loudly *PUTAIN DE MERDE*. Which means *whore of shit* but is like saying *fucking hell*. Poor M. When I ask through my laughter if there was a queue, he says only an old lady. But it was like he'd let off an explosive, the effect it had on the surroundings.

It feels so good to laugh. I want to ask him more questions but he has to run off to an indoor basketball game with Dan and a group of guys down the canal.

'Will you stay here tonight?' he asks.

There is such sweetness in his question my heart feels sore. I know he is not asking out of need, but care. He knows today would have been hard.

JAYNE:
Yes. I'm sorry I've been so absent.

M:

It's fine, you need to take your space. But it will be good to have
you here.

He comes and wraps his arms around me. I hug him back.

M:

One good piece of news. I got the last letter today. That part of the
work is done. I'm going to see Hogarth tomorrow to deliver the file.

JAYNE:

Thank God.

M:

One huge box ticked. Then it's just the last big
one and it's done. Well done. You're so close now.

The building. Beyond that black hole, a glimmer of light.

JAYNE:

Thank you so much.

As he gets up and clears our dishes I think of the letters. What has
he seen? What do they contain? He kisses me, puts his sneakers on
and leaves.

M:

Back around 9. We can watch *The Wire*.

As soon as he's gone I'm ransacking the apartment, I have to see them.
Be careful what you let into yourself. Fuck off Adrien. The private
investigator needs to know. I don't have to look far, he has felt no reason
to hide them, trusting I have no interest in reading them. They are in
a box on his side of the closet.

Letters from doctors talking about lasting postural damage, a likelihood of ongoing lifetime pain, future need for plastic surgery, skin tissue crush injury. Good name for a metal band, M would say.

Bérénice: *at the lightest touch she would howl, has remained in constant pain ... She still wears a tight scarf though she doesn't need to ...*

A letter from Daphné saying she has dropped me from her books as I have lost my ability to perform and the facial scars will limit roles in film and television, not only because of the way they look but the muscular damage causing a lessened expressive range ... – I didn't know I was dumped!

A letter from Tez saying my career is over, that I tried to direct a play, but it failed due to my physical and mental weakness.

A letter from Kiki saying my personality changed after the accident, she didn't recognise me anymore. My face even looked different post-surgery leading no doubt to future difficulties in my acting career. Extreme behaviour. Morbid thoughts.

Madame Lecoq: *a most promising student, with potentially a brilliant career ahead, cruelly cut short by this monstrous accident ...*

Nadine writes that I was once an outgoing, exuberant person, now I'm introverted and reclusive, irritable in ways I never was before; she's sad to say my comportment changed, in the way that someone you know suddenly seems like someone else, trouble focusing, unable to concentrate for the length of a conversation ...

Marie-France describes a person horribly disfigured, incapacitated, different to before, no future as an actress, permanently damaged, anxious, nervous, delusional. *She used to do the most beautiful cartwheels. Now she will never cartwheel again.*

Faye describes someone that once was funny, outgoing and wildly creative, now morose and shy.

Antoine describes the horror of learning what had happened, and how I wouldn't be able to fulfil my role in the marionette show I'd been cast in. He doesn't mention the new play.

Detailed letters from my dad, my sister, listing the costs incurred to them for flights, medical care, my sister having to defer her university year, loss of income. Emotional deterioration post the accident, illness, anorexia. Dad describes erratic behaviour, violent outbursts, depression. Obsession with the macabre, morbid research. Fascination with death and decapitation.

The French doctor describes how the triangular skin flap has 'trapdoored' which may require more surgery, chronic post traumatic nerve root pain.

An account from the Geelong hospital describes a terribly ill patient that refused to eat – liver failure – screaming and night terrors – flashbacks to the stairwell and the near-death experience, lacerations …

The psychiatrist in Melbourne: *Her career as an actress is over – cruelly stripped by this hideous accident. She was in effect an actor in a circus-like theatre; an occupation demanding extraordinary fitness and strength, both at body and emotional levels, which probably prevented her death. She should have expected to earn the same sort of reputation and money as somebody of the calibre of Cate Blanchett, but now, with her facial scar, physical ailments and psychological limitations, she will have to consider alternatives. Somehow avoiding decapitation by the lift, which acted as a form of guillotine, was the factor that precipitated her ongoing life being shunted into a totally different direction.*

Adrien's is the only one that's kind.

Jayne was courageous through the surgery procedures and though afraid, strong and in a positive state of mind. I tried to play down the extent of her injuries so as not to worry her. Others around her were very concerned. When I left her at the hospital she was happy and calm. I knew she would be fine, she is a strong woman. I stayed with her the entire night until morning and was assured that her recovery would not be difficult, that she would regain her full movement and her face would heal.

At the bottom of the box, a letter from M.

Though I met Jayne after the accident, I have noticed a decline in her mental health since: anxiety, claustrophobia, agoraphobia, inability to be touched, sexual dysfunction. We had hoped to be in a relationship together but the longer she lives with the trauma of the accident, the more that seems impossible. Really, it has been impossible for her emotionally to be vulnerable in any way. She is constantly afraid. When she walks down the street in the daytime she sees things – accidents happening everywhere she looks – constant horrors – after witnessing a small mishap on a crossing she reacted as though the children had been crushed, though I had managed to stop the truck driver moving forward and the children were unharmed, aside from a small cut. In fact to her that was what she truly saw.

I know she suffers constant pain though she is determined to keep this from me and all those who love her.

I close the box.

⌒

I leave a note that night that I have gone to Marie-France's. That all is fine, I just need a few days before the final tick to pull myself together. It feels terrible to leave. Later that night, snuggled in Marie-France's *couette* I get a message from M:

I miss you. This will all be over soon. Remember it's a game, none of it is real. One last box to tick and all will be more wonderful than you could ever have imagined. If I don't hear from you, I will meet you at métro Gambetta at 9:50 on Wednesday. M x

I'm the criminal. It is me that should be sued. Putting M through this. Asking people to say such things. They're not true. Are they? I'm a fraud. What *is* true? There are problems. There are limitations. But I can get through them. I *will* act again. I will cartwheel again. I'll get my life back to where it was. I'm so grateful, so lucky. It's not doom and gloom. This is horrible. I should never have done this. But the boy. Oh the boy!

Can't sleep.

The next two days are a blur. On Monday I write a brochure about baths that change colour, see a movie, take the line 3 to Pont de Levallois to visit Marie-France and Emma, take a sweet walk in a very neat park, trying to forget about her letter, but not being able to trust now what she thinks of me. Marie-France is coming back to a central place of happiness and longing to return to acting and her apartment. Emma is already far prettier, her puckered face stretching out with the passing days. I still fear to hold her, my hands tremble too much. I don't stay long, wandering back over the *périphérique* and into the city.

Mad people are sensing me everywhere. Outside the Opéra métro, an old woman swamped in piles of torn clothes asks me politely, '*Excusez-moi mademoiselle*, what day is it?' and I say 'Monday' and she says 'Oh I thought it was Tuesday – no wonder there's trains!' I know what you mean, I say, as she walks off.

In the crowded train carriage a man comes up from behind me and screams that he's going to CUT MY FUCKING HEAD OFF. I am so shaken I get off at Bonne Nouvelle and sit on a seat for ten minutes before getting back on the train.

Smell of old piss. Homeless Adrien. French M going past in a carriage with his arm around a cute Parisienne.

The bunny on the sticker next to the train door says to be careful not to put your hands in the doorway, *tu risques de te faire pincer tres fort.*

The bunny has a funny expression on his face with an explosion coming out of his hand to illustrate the pain. I see people stuck in those doors all the time, heads caught, dragged along the platform. The *pince*. *Très fort*. There is no sensor. Nothing to stop you falling down the gap at the Gare du Nord.

At the crossing as I approach Marie-France's door, a man on a bike calls out to me:

'Eh! *Où es-tu?*'

Where am I?

Exactly.

Marie-France's bathroom. Skin caviar. Your senses feel caressed by an extravagant gift of energy and moisture. Step beyond ordinary luxury into the ultimate caviar collection … neither your skin nor your psyche will ever be the same.

The urge to call Kiki:

'*Merrrde* fuckface it's 6 am. Are you okay what's happening with the lawsuit is M still there how is it going do you think you did the right thing how are you getting by can you get me some more grey hair from the boulevard I don't have enough for the show are you out of Vegemite is your dad okay, when are you coming home —'

To hear her voice feels like making contact with the home planet from outer space. She thought she was pregnant but she's not. Am I in love?

'Wish you were here.'

Tuesday. A boardroom full of people in suits. Tall bottles of Evian in the middle of the table, Coca Zero, smell of tobacco, perfume and new chairs. Léa the designer uses Fructis to wash her hair. I can smell everything. My stomach turns as the businesspeople discuss the project, asking questions I can't follow, answering in long sentences with serious faces. I nod when required, lips pursed, brow furrowed. I am wearing my glasses. My outfit has been dry-cleaned and the hole in my stocking is below the seam though I tried to hide it. Chipped red nail polish. Léa adds a comment here and there, there seems to be some debate. I think of asking them to clarify what they just said but my body just nods again, hand props my face. Someone says something that's directed at me and Henri the taller bald creative director asks me to comment. I have the gist – they're not sure about the concept we've come up with, so I stand with the mock-up of the booklet Léa has designed and start to explain it. Something comes over me, a businessperson steps into my body and the language coming out of my mouth belongs to her. I want to laugh at the person speaking, so far from the truth of who I am, a confident person speaking high French with the same accent as everyone else. With the requisite joining words, pouts and sighs to accentuate the parts that require accentuating, fluctuations in tone, never allowing the smiling Australian modulation to enter her voice, keeping it good and flat and clear – nothing to argue with here, this chick knows her shit.

The businesspeople listen in silence until I'm finished, saying *merci Jayne c'est très bien* before turning back to the bald guys and discussing the finer points. I sit, flushed. Léa looks at me, eyes wide. Perhaps I went too far. Where did I pick that up? I must have been collating this character without realising, for some time, in preparation for this moment. I'm not sure if the content of what I said was enough to sell the brochure, but after the clients are gone, the directors and Léa breathe out and say *top*, it's a done deal, brava Jayne. What a show. Claude would have clapped long and loud.

D-Day

Wednesday October 28th, 10 am. *Convocation*, 26-28 rue Pelleport, Paris 75020.

M is waiting at the top of the Gambetta métro, out the front of the brasserie that Sophie and I would do our 'English classes' in sometimes. Though this part of Paris has been frozen in my mind, it is as convivial and active as it always was. Mounting the steps, I do not die.

It's cold. I'm in costume – greasy hair, no makeup, dirty sneakers, Aspen collar. I want it over. M takes me straight into his warm winter coat and walks me down the boulevard. Hogarth has said to arrive at 10:05, for dramatic effect. I am playing a role but I also *am* the role. Is this method acting? I want to faint. I want to die. I want to be anywhere but here, on the rue Pelleport, walking to Sophie's old building.

We arrive in the street, a few buildings up from Sophie's on its corner. Thank goodness Sophie and her family are far from here. My character is trembling, emaciated, eviscerated. M holds my clammy hand tight. The sun is out. Ahead on the corner outside Sophie's building stand a dozen men of varying shapes and sizes, shielding their eyes from the bright autumn sun with clipboards and briefcases.

This is it. *Le Jour-J.* The last box. There is nothing of me left. I've done it all, tainted my acting career if not destroyed it, humiliated and exposed myself, put my dignity and wellbeing on the line, and now I'm about to step into my nightmare.

Where is Hogarth?

Slugworth sidles up beside me and offers another obsequious greeting with his sluggy little grin. I would like to spontaneously vomit like Camus' dad right into his mouth, all the bile, the *vénale* intention I have for him, this system, this entire experience.

A man steps forward and introduces himself as from the company here to assess the situation of the lift. Then other men come up and introduce themselves, lawyers, someone from the *copropriété*, someone from an insurance company, more men and more men. I shake their hands and say *bonjour* in a feeble voice over and over.

No sign of Hogarth. We wander the corner, waiting. After ten minutes the men say we can't wait any longer and go to move inside. I give M a desperate look. He has been trying Hogarth but there's no answer.

We have to go in.

When I was eleven Dad took me out of school one day to visit the Melbourne Museum. There was an exhibition on called *Devils Drugs and Doctors* – a history of the science of medicine. It was super gory, with installations about leeches and witchcraft and medicine men. Now I think of it, it seems like an extreme thing to take me to, but I had such a fascination with science and the body, he must have thought I'd love it. There was one room I've never forgotten. It smelled like formaldehyde and dust and showed motorised dummies enacting a leg amputation. There was a sound recording of the saw going back and forward over a man's leg, and of his screams; his shocked, conscious face visible through slits in the cloth as a female dummy fainted over and over again. I remember feeling out of place, watching something so terrifying and intimate, even if they were dummies. It seemed absurd to be standing there, witnessing someone else's horror. The smell and feel of that exhibition is what it feels like to step into Sophie's building. I am entering a place of physical hell and also the dustiest, darkest place in my psyche. A death exhibition, open to the public.

We step inside the building. Everything is the same as on the night of the accident. The foyer is just as I remember. Same black-and-white chequered floor, same gilded mirror, same lift well with intricate black ironwork set in the middle of the stairs. Same stairwell, same darkness, though it's morning. *In for four, hold for seven …*

The men walk up the stairs. We watch them before following, arms against the walls. In the middle of the stairwell, the lift cage. The banister with its protective grille at a height meant for mid-century French people, not late-century Australians (in boots). Being here is to live inside a memory, to not be present. Would they make someone who was almost killed in a car accident return to the road where it happened and play it out? *Accident de ski*, the slope? I am nauseous. Can't feel my feet. The men's chatter echoes through the cavern, dampened by the thick red carpet.

I'm back on that night. Dark January, the soft, red stairs, Sophie and Lou's voices in the stairwell as they walked up to meet me. The feeling of warmth, family, a little girl that had taken to me, her dumpling arms around my neck.

The men wander up and down the stairs, looking around while keeping well away from the lift shaft and the banister. M and I sit on a stair somewhere between the first and second floor, my right side as far from the lift as possible, pressed up against the wall. I close my eyes and try to breathe.

After they've looked and written down notes, the lift expert asks the other men to come towards me on the stairwell in order to ask me a question.

THE LIFT EXPERT:
Alors Madame Tuttle. Please explain to us as clearly as you can
what happened on the night of January 18.

I tell them in French the speech I've said a thousand times. The men nod and take notes though they all must have read this in my *témoignage*. Either way I'm glad nothing much is happening without Hogarth here,

I feel insecure without him. Where on earth is he? This wasn't part of the staging. This is the moment I need him most.

LIFT EXPERT:
Can you please show us what happened leading up to
the accident?

JAYNE:
Do you mean, play it out for you?

LIFT EXPERT:
Yes please.

I look at M. 'It's a performance,' he says. 'Just take it moment by moment. But don't do anything you don't want to do.'
'The actor is always laughing.'
I stand up.

JAYNE:
So. I ran up here. Then I rang the doorbell and waited.

On Sophie and Fréd's *sonnette* now it reads 'BONNET-VERNIER'.

Nobody was home, which was strange, I was on time,
6 o'clock. So I stood here and rang Sophie.

I pretend to call Sophie.

She told me she was just entering the building, and we hung
up. I heard them come in downstairs. I could see them from
the stairwell walking across the foyer, without leaning over.
I walked down a few steps and called 'Lou!' She looked up,
trying to find me.

This is the dumbest play I've ever been in. The *profs* at Lecoq would have already called '*Merci – next!*' It's so obvious what's going to happen and they all already know. But I keep going with the demonstration.

> Lou was saying *où est Jayne?* So I played a little game with her, calling her name then stepping back, then I looked over the banister.

I don't demonstrate this action, I stand well back from the banister, against the wall, and point to where I leant over.

> That was when I noticed my head was jammed. I couldn't breathe or call out, I could see them walking up the stairs. Then I felt a huge roar, then I must have pulled my head out from beneath and passed out.

The lift expert says *Merci Madame Tuttle*, then he calls out loudly to everyone standing on the stairwell to stand right back, they are going to call the lift, first from the bottom floor to the top on the 8th floor, then from the top to the bottom. EVERYONE STAND RIGHT BACK.

M whispers to me, 'If it's not dangerous why do they need to stand back?'

We stand on the stairwell, backs pressed to the walls. *ET UN, DEUX TROIS, POUSSER.* The lift rises from the *rez-de-chaussée*, passing us in almost total silence. There is not even a *whoosh*. Even in broad daylight, the lift well is so dark you can also barely see it moving, nor its pulleys and cables. It's terrifying. The men peel themselves away from the wall to mumble and make notes.

The lift expert then repeats the same procedure, and once all the safety measures are checked and the lift on the 8th floor, shouts for everyone to stand back. We wait in silence, pressed against the solidity of the cool cement. As the lift passes there is an audible gasp from several of the men. I am nauseated. The descending lift, passing the diagonal rail, gives the effect of a guillotine falling. A silence. Nobody moves for a moment. Then more notes and mumbling.

LIFT EXPERT:
And now, the same thing from the top of the building, to
the second floor.

One of the men goes and presses the call button on the second floor.

EVERYONE STAND RIGHT BACK.

The lift rises to the top floor again. Then we watch with horror as it comes to stop at the level halfway down the stairs between the first and second floor where we are standing, leaving a small triangular gap between the banister and the bottom of the lift. This must be where my head got stuck. Is that possible? The gap doesn't seem big enough for a head. Just enough for a neck, perhaps.

I sit down on the stairwell. M rubs my shoulders.

LIFT EXPERT:
Now we will send the lift to the bottom from here. Then
Madame Tuttle will show us how she leant over.

JAYNE:
You mean lean over the banister?

LIFT EXPERT:
Précisément.

JAYNE:
Oh god. I'm sorry, I can't.

M:
She can't of course. I will do it.

JAYNE:
No! Don't do it! Please!

M:
It will be safe, don't worry.

JAYNE:
I don't even want you to do it for fun.

M:
It is not fun, believe me. But they do need to see how your
body could come over the banister.

They are more than cautious this time. The lift is safely on the *rez-de-chaussée* and a man at each level to ensure no call button is pressed during the exercise. Three men verify that the lift is on the ground floor before, surrounded by the lift expert and four other men, M leans over the banister as if he was calling out to below.

Watching him lean over so easily fills me with equal amounts of relief and terror. It looks perfectly natural, so easy. Not a suicidal gesture. Something anyone would do, any time. Or is it just an Australian thing? Our houses, with stairs?

M is made to repeat the gesture over and over again until they're satisfied. Mumbling and notes, walking up and down the stairs. I think it's done. It must be done now.

A man I don't remember seeing before walks up the stairwell to where I am sitting.

UNFAMILIAR MAN:
So, you called the lift on that night from the 2nd floor, and
that's why it stopped.

JAYNE:
No, I never called the lift.

UNFAMILIAR MAN:
You must have, otherwise why did it stop?

JAYNE:
I don't know. But I didn't call it.

UNFAMILIAR MAN:
Your friends weren't home. Nobody else lives on this floor.
You must have pressed the button.

JAYNE:
I know for a fact I didn't. Why would I have? I was walking
down the stairs.

UNFAMILIAR MAN:
Perhaps you mistook it for the light switch.

JAYNE:
But the button is all the way over there! No, I just started walking
down as soon as I heard them. Perhaps the lift had a sensor.

UNFAMILIAR MAN:
(*laughing*)
This is a very old lift, there is nothing like that. And we have
done a thorough investigation which revealed no faults
with the lift's functioning, so it could only have stopped if it
was called.

JAYNE:
Well, I remember this powerful feeling rising in me, like a train
coming. Is it possible I stopped the lift with my will to live?

UNFAMILIAR MAN:
(*laughing more*)

The lift weighs half a tonne. There is no way this is
humanly possible.

JAYNE:
I one hundred per cent did not press that button.

UNFAMILIAR MAN:
Then who did?

Mum?
Another man walks up the stairs to me, in a pinstripe grey suit.

GREY SUIT MAN:
We need you to show us yourself what happened.

I translate what they are saying to M and he responds to them
in English.

M:
No. It's obvious, as I just showed you. We're the same
height. Look where she is standing. She just has to lean this
way and she's over.

SLUGWORTH:
It's okay, you don't need to show. We can go now.

Slugworth wouldn't say that unless there was something for him to
gain in me not showing them. What was it? Then it occurs to me. My
height. M and I are the same height. On the night of the accident I
was wearing 5 centimetre high heels. It looked easy for M to lean over
the banister, but with the extra height it would feel even more normal
a gesture.

A voice booms from the first floor. Hogarth.

HOGARTH:

Qu'est-ce qui se passe ici?

He is standing at the bottom of the stairwell looking up. He looks a million bucks in a fantastic navy suit.

HOGARTH:

What are you doing to this poor girl? She nearly died here – are you seriously asking her to repeat the same actions? Are you all insane? This country, I swear! It's barbaric! Sit down, poor girl. Sit down and recover your breath.

I weep into my hands. Is it acting? I don't think so. Is it that Hogarth is protecting me? Is it the feeling of being protected?

Hogarth comes and sits down next to me, whispering.

HOGARTH:

Now girl, you have to show them. This is all a good performance you're doing. Take your time. But you have got to show them. It's powerful that they see you, a female, performing the action that caused all this. They need to see it in your body. And why on earth didn't you bring the boots you wore that night?

JAYNE:

I don't have them in France.

Hogarth turns around and booms in French:

HOGARTH:

On the night of the accident Madame Tuttle was wearing 5 centimetre high heels. It has been submitted in evidence. She was in fact taller than her boyfriend here, who has kindly demonstrated the action leading to the horror.

Hogarth returns to pep-talk me. *Do this one last thing. Then it is over.* M rubs my back. I stand and walk to the level on the staircase where it happened. Men shout up and down the stairwell. The lift is sitting safely, innocently, grounded on the *rez-de-chaussée.* I go to the edge of the stairs and put my hands on the rail. The ghost of Lou calls me from below. I stand on the balls of my feet, to show the height of the heels. Then I lean over, into the void.

JAYNE:

Looo-ou! Hey, Lou!!

And here I am. At home, on the stairs, calling *MUM! WHAT'S FOR DINNER?* Or for Kate to come upstairs and play, or leaning over to roar at my brothers, the trolls lurking beneath. No wonder I did it. The move is as natural to me as a cartwheel.

Time slows down, like it must have that night. The two of them walking up the stairs seemed to go for minutes. Perhaps it was a fraction of a second before I yanked my head out. It must have been quick. Lou is there, face an orb of light, I know she was drawing me to death, I feel it any time I think of her. It was peaceful and beautiful, and I wasn't worried at all. It's a nice thing to know. A dream most certainly. But more than that.

I am pulled back from the void. Arms surround me and I'm whisked downstairs and outside into the daylight.

HOGARTH:

Okay, that's over with. You did it. Good girl, bravo. Go home
and forget about it all now. I'll be in touch.

M and I return to Annelets. I take off the neck brace and throw it dramatically in the bin, knowing I'll fish it out again because I need it. M puts on music and starts making some food and I take a long, long shower and put on the softest things I own, and for some reason, bright red lipstick.

Hogarth calls a few days later to say congratulations for the tour de force – it came across exceptionally well that I was traumatised on that stairwell! Hahaha. And that my part is over, I can retire my acting role.

A great sense of peace washes over me.

Also, good news. He has received word that the owners of the building and their insurers will accept responsibility. He is awaiting the formal documents. The payout will be small, around the amount he first wrote down. He recognises this will barely cover the legal and hospital costs, but we should take it, there is little chance of gaining more.

The point is, they have accepted fault and will address the danger. I did it. I got what I wanted. Aren't I glad?

I thank him and hang up, not sure what to say.

I am glad I did it. Not to acknowledge it and pick at every scab, uncover every clue as to what happened, how it happened and why, might have left questions in my mind that ate away at me throughout the rest of my life. So much remains unanswered; I still don't understand how I was able to get my head out of that small triangular gap and how and why the lift stopped above my head, but I'd rather have those questions hanging over me than whether I should have made an effort to defend myself and protect other people. Life is weird, I know that, and unpredictable, and Paris is beautiful and beauty is dangerous, but still … I'm glad to have stopped and stared it down.

Paris is laughing, the devil. This is not the first curve ball she's thrown at me, nor will it be her last. I feel connected to her despite it all, more than ever. She seems to be my guide, a mother figure, albeit a conflicted and imperfect one, and though she may be modified for safety, and life will keep throwing its own curve balls at her, she will always be the same.

Perhaps I wanted to do the lawsuit because it was weird and ugly and painful and intriguing. Perhaps I wanted to do it so I could write this book. Perhaps the struggle makes things interesting. If Winnie could step out of her mound, there would be no Winnie. If everything in Paris was 100% safe, it wouldn't be Paris.

Perhaps I am glad the accident happened. It woke me up from the trajectory I was on – a kamikaze hurtling towards the abyss. It made me stop, slowed me down, allowed me to feel the simple beating of my heart. I got to see the end of life and come back, and keep my senses and functioning. I got to live. I got to move. I discovered writing.

And I got to meet someone. Really meet them.

The Clearing

The smoking ban transforms Paris. The city's interiors, once cloaked in a perpetual romantic haze are now stark, colourful, in focus. You can see things. Café floors once carpeted in ash and butts suddenly reveal themselves as dancing mosaics. Bar tops in the morning no longer prop the scabby elbows of elderly gents clutching early beers, but the rears of young children nursing *orange pressée*. Country-wide, local *tabacs* close their doors – betting on horses and drinking beer is not something done *sans clope*. It's winter, temperatures are freezing, and in the streets, smokers crowd around doorways and on *terrasses*, chattering in their coats and scarves. In restaurants you can taste better. You can definitely smell better – not always a good thing.

It's strange, and I'm not sure I like it. Half the magic of Paris for me had come with seeing it through the waxed lens of smoke. Paris with Adrien was all about smoking: impossible to imagine it without that fog. It thickened the air, kept things blurred, mysterious. The ban seems at odds with the soul of the city – about living life with a touch of blindness, and enjoying it. We're all going to die. Might as well smoke, eat goose fat, ride your bike sans helmet, walk beneath pot plants every day.

My senses feel enhanced. Not just because of the lack of smoke, but because the lawsuit is over. I read in the newspaper that the boy's parents also sued their building and will receive just a little more than me for the death of their son. I wondered if my case had helped them in any way. I hope so. I hope they know he wasn't alone.

I told M I'd read the letters, and it made him sad. Not because I hadn't followed the plan but because I'd seen the words. He took my hand and told me what he wrote was pure fiction, to not believe a word of it. It was only written for the performance, all the letters were. I was to delete them from my mind. To not let them in. I'm trying. The confusion is still there over what the true impact was and what the lasting effects will be. But as the days go by a lightness is coming, a feeling of clarity.

Here at the Carillon with M, all is crisp, the colours brighter; I can see the outlines of things: the cracks in the table, the tiled floor in orange, red and yellow, Jean's face at the markets across the street. My hearing is better. I feel less disoriented, less worried something is going to fall on my head, though the awareness is always there of the great arsenic lobster that could fall at any moment from the sky.

M sips his dreadful over-moussed *café crème* while thumbing the *Libération,* asking random questions of comprehension. His powers of deduction from years of crosswords, along with his now decent grammar has brought his French up to a standard that is opening the city out to him in constant new ways. He wants to open a café. Write an album with the band. Finally complete the basic administrative task of securing an international driver's license. He still loves it here as much as I do. He understands how even after the accident and the nightmare of the lawsuit, things are not black and white. He looks up at me.

'What are you thinking about?'

'Oh, just about smoking,' I say. 'Now we're not allowed, I really want one.'

'Too bad, banned,' he says, and goes back to his reading.

What I'm actually thinking is this. I love him. I love how he has never, right from the beginning, pressured me to be anyone but myself, or to do anything for him. And that is not the reason why I love him. I love him because he is the person that doesn't need those things from anybody at all. Not once in these two hellish years has he needed me to be a certain way, or tried to influence me or change me. He met me at my worst and let me be, allowed me to stumble my way through the fog, which I needed to do, holding his hand out for me to grab when I wanted it. He was content to build his own life beside me and be my friend, accept me as I was, without expectation, with freedom. Now I can sit here and look at his gentle face and love him the way I want, free of the pain. Or with the pain, if it's there, that's okay too. I never knew you could be together with someone and feel so free. I feel so free with him the idea of being without him is suffocating.

We decide to walk across the canal to the bookshop, and stop at the top of the Bridge of Atmosphère to watch the swing bridge open. The traffic is stopped on either side as the road cracks and turns to let the water rush in so a canal boat full of people can move slowly through the water, looking trapped and exposed. I must have crossed this bridge a thousand times, with Kiki, Adrien, Kate, Harry, and most of all with M. We always stop here at the top to watch the boats pass and observe the changes in the water, from murky brown in autumn to slimy green in summer to frozen grey in winter. We watch the ducks, the pigeons, the different kinds of people lounging on the banks, the guy eating the kebab we then go and buy for ourselves. We look up the canal towards the La Villette, and down the canal towards the Seine. We drag our caddy over the rickety slats when the straight route across has turned, sucking on clementines or strawberries from the market, taking the things we've bought over to the Jardin Villemin for lunch. I've been so many people here on this bridge: a lonely student living in the Récollets for the first time, a broken person returning to Paris to stay with Nadine after the recovery, a drunk necking warm champagne with Kiki from the bottle, a heartbroken lover wanting to hurl myself off. It's where we would picnic as students, where Harry jumped into the filthy water one summer, where M and I saw two boys nearly crushed by a truck down there on the crossing. The bridge is not perfect, there is sadness and pain and history and life in it. It is the small part of Paris that I realise means the most to me.

On a rainy night, in a few weeks' time, I will kneel here at the top of the bridge and ask M to marry me. Gobsmacked, he will say yes. And as if Paris has let us go, the Dodger will call to say that the betting syndicate is closing down, fast; Annelets and all the apartments will be dissolved, and within weeks M will find himself out of a home, job and income. We will move to Harry's while he's on a shoot in Africa and spend days on rental sites, trying to compile the paperwork we don't have, waving goodbye to the Dodger who will return to London, and Dan who will move back to Austin. M will advertise on Craigslist for a new drummer and a new job. Nothing will seem to work. Things will feel stopped, like Paris is no longer guiding us. It will remind me of the feeling I had that day when I called Dad from the tomb in the Père Lachaise, such a pull to return to Australia that I denied in order to push towards what I perceived was my destiny, compacting my will into such a tight ball I almost ended up dead. Paris has her own plans. She is done with us for now.

Dad will meet us at the airport. I will meet M's family, he will meet the rest of mine. We will live for a time in M's tiny flat full of guitar leads and amps and a printer. I will work on the book, that gets further from being finished the more I write it. The play will stay fuming in a drawer, acting roles will come, mostly voice-overs for French yoghurt companies. M will make a new album with his old band. There will be cartwheels.

But not yet. We are still here, on the bridge watching the canal boats, and he is turning to kiss me and I'm kissing him back, longer than usual, until a passing local tells us to get a room, fucking tourists.

⁓

Tonight is the opening of the marionette show. Weeks ago, before the visit to Sophie's building, I'd received a purple envelope with the invite inside to the opening of *Alice Sans Grace*: a postcard with a collage design of faces stuck on various cut-up bodies against a vibrant purple background. I had hidden it in my underwear drawer, still afraid to go to the 20th, and ashamed to have missed the show's entire development. M did a load of washing, found the invitation and insisted we invite our friends and make a night of it. Now the lawsuit is over, I feel differently about going. Nervous still, but not in a death-panic. An alert switch in my brain seems to have been turned off. All this time avoiding the 20th. That part of Paris I loved so much, my little apartment in the rue de la Chine above the restaurant, the owner Luc always inviting me down for wine, which I never drank. The cobblestone lanes, the cats in windows, coming home to my quiet place to put some food in my fridge, to sit and read, free and alone.

We return to Annelets late in the afternoon to eat an early dinner and get dressed for the show. I spend a long time deciding what to wear. M emerges in his dapper suit, with a new felt hat. I choose not to wear a scarf, though it's cold.

We decide to walk. The night is cool and still as we walk up Annelets to the rue de la Villette, where fairy lights are strung above the street. We take the rue des Pyrénées up to the rue de la Chine and down the unremarkable street to my old building where someone else is moving around behind the windows on the first floor, their pot plants looking safe. Downstairs, the restaurant is being set up for dinner. M and I go inside and sit at the bar. Luc stops wiping a glass. Jayne! He comes around and kisses me, looking me over. I remember Luc's face when I returned to the building in a stretcher. Then, when they put me in the ambulance to go to the airport, different that time, sad and confused. Now he pours M and me both a glass of champagne, asking us questions between shouting orders and passing drinks across the bar. I tell him the whole story. It feels amazing to say it out loud, to describe it, feeling no need to act.

Afterwards, holding hands, M and I walk down the Avenue Gambetta, and down the rue Pelleport past Sophie's building. We don't stop, but it's not that we hurry past, we are just en route to the theatre. It's okay. It's a building. Soon it will be made safe.

We pass the Hôpital Tenon, the place they first brought me after the accident, and where there had been an electrical issue and the lights strobed on and off as they tried to figure out what had happened to me. I tell M all that I remember, the howling man, Adrien's calm voice, how they weren't equipped to handle my situation so I was transported to Salpêtrière with no idea what was going on. He listens. They do walking tours around here telling people old stories of the 20th; Piaf, Perec, Gainsbourg. I'm giving M a ghost tour of me. These places have lived in a different part of me until now, deep in my consciousness. It feels good to see they're just places, bricks and grout and cigarette butts.

Our friends are already in the foyer of the theatre when we arrive. Nadine and Didier are squeezed together; they've recently moved in together to a place in the 10th. Charles is back and he and Valentin are looking at venues to open a restaurant (one of Charles' books has struck a chord in Korea), Fanny is there, she's famous now, star of a TV crime series. Marie-France and Hakim are there without the dropped pie. The band guys and their girlfriends are there. The Dodger is drinking champagne. The theatre is full and cosy and loud. Marie-France says she's nervous for me to see what the show has become, what if I think it's a shitpile? Antoine hurries up to us on his way backstage – *bienvenue, bienvenue!* Take your seats!

The show is something I could never have imagined; in French as vulgar and weird as what I wrote – Marie-France has even injected some wicked English swearing – but utterly unique in its French voice. Six *marionnettistes* create all the different characters and scenography, using dolls and projections and shadows; the characters fly and fuck and split and morph and die, they are silly, dreamy, sad. Though they are far from what I wrote, which was based on something I didn't understand, I see my life in them, my people: M in Grace, Kiki in the funny, naughty Alice. There is Mum in Lone Man Lost in Solitude, Nadine in the wise Black Cat. Adrien in Arseface.

At the end the crowd applauds with vigour, until they do that weird French thing where they get into a rhythm. Antoine comes on stage to join the cast and they salute the technicians and then they salute Marie-France, who salutes me. We all clap wildly, we are proud. I think it was *juste*. Marie-France thinks so too. Perhaps there was even *duende*.

As we're leaving, Antoine comes rushing out to ask us all for drinks with the cast. At the Bistrot 1929. There is no *andouillette* but there is drinking and dancing until late in the night.

I look at M and see how happy he is. We're going to live here forever.

Acknowledgements

Thank you first and foremost to Matt Davis. No work of mine, and especially this one, would have found its way into the world without his constant creative input and unwavering support.

Thank you to Frankie Davis, for her wisdom, her understanding, her kindness, her small hands on my neck, *go mama*.

My deepest gratitude to Arwen Summers, Meredith Rose, Jane Novak, Brooke Munday, Amy Petrovich, France Lane, Melissa Kayser, Carol Major, Anna Elliot, Jemma Birrell, Mary Kelly, Marisa Purcell, Kate van den Boogert, Joshua Croggon, Rachel Mogan-McIntosh, Martine Murray, Libby Little, Lauren Elkin, Elsa Morgan, Leigh Whannell, Corbett Tuck, Luke Milne, Florian Cadiou, Pauline Parker, Rachael Coopes, Chrystel Dozias, Pascale Lecoq, the Davis family, John, Rod and Andy Tuttle and the forever-missed Lyn Tuttle.

Thank you to the Varuna Writer's House and the Dark family for the generosity and support of the Eric Dark Flagship Fellowship.

This book was mostly written on the land of the Wadawurrung people. I offer my gratitude and respect to the elders of this land and to all First Nations people past and present.